MW01079720

About the Author

Tony was born in Lowell, Mass., September 17, 1920, and grew up in Lewiston, Maine where the first signs of his addiction to building and flying surfaced in his early teens.

His very first project was a Knight Twister followed by a Pou du Ciel (Flying Flea). Unfortunately, neither project was completed because the available $2.50 building fund ran out.

Not one to squander hard earned cash, Tony used the Flying Flea wing ribs, and rudder, around which to design a primary glider. It, more or less, broke ground in a couple of early flight attempts. Fortunately, a hurricane did what Tony failed to do . . . destroyed the glider.

In 1940, soon after graduating from school, Tony enlisted in the U.S. Army Air Corps and shipped out to Panama where he attended an Aircraft Mechanics course and Weather Observer course among other intellectual pursuits. He discovered going to school was easier than working.

Tony obtained his Aviation Cadet appointment while in Panama and was ultimately shipped to the U.S. for cadet training.

In Uvalde, Texas he was assigned a crop duster pilot, an instructor who managed to solo Tony in the PT-19 as scheduled.

Training continued with Basic in San Angelo and Advanced in Mission/McAllen, Texas . . . in T-6's.

In 1943 he was duly commissioned a second lieutenant and declared a pilot and he was sent to Randolph Field to learn how to teach others to fly BT-13's.

Then, it was back to San Angelo to practice his newly acquired talents as a flight instructor.

After deciding that was a suicidal wartime occupation, Tony volunteered for a secret mission . . . glider training in CG4A's with the avowed purpose of invading Germany and winning the war.

Luckily, he had too much flying time to waste and they put him in the right seat of a C-47 to haul supplies all over England, Belgium, France and Germany.

The postwar years passed quickly and Tony found himself doing odd jobs like operating a helicopter mechanic school in Biloxi and Wichita Falls, training liaison pilots in San Marcos, Texas, attending the National Aquatic Swimming School in Palo Pinto, Texas, the Command and Staff School in Alabama, and studying Japanese at the Foreign Service Institute in Washington. Then, much to his surprise, he was shipped out to Japan . . . not to South America as he expected.

In Japan in 1960, Tony started his first to-be-completed homebuilt, an Emeraude, in a clothes closet workshop.

The Emeraude was finished in Texas six years later.

This project was followed closely, by a Flaglor Scooter, a Volksplane, a Turner T-40, another Emeraude, a Falco, and all of the RV series homebuilts.

Tony's philosophy was and still is . . . if you are going to write about building homebuilts you had better be a builder yourself. A somewhat better builder than he is a pilot, Tony, nevertheless, blissfully, opted to test fly each of his own homebuilts.

Tony has long been a supportive member of the EAA and has volunteered his services since the early '50's in a number of capacities, each revolving around the homebuilt activities of the EAA. Early in 1972, he was asked to write three articles for SPORT AVIATION and now, 22 years later, he is still meeting that relentless monthly schedule.

Tony's first three books on homebuilding practices have become classics and are eagerly sought by new builders.

Hopefully, this latest book, based on much of the information printed in his SPORT AVIATION articles over the past 10 years, will receive the same welcome by builders worldwide.

TONY BINGELIS
ON
ENGINES

Engine Compartment Installations for Sportplane Builders

by Tony Bingelis

(Article Photos and Drawings by the Author)

Edited and Prepared by S. H. "Wes" Schmid
Publisher Tom Poberezny, EAA Aviation Foundation
Printed by Times Printing Company, Random Lake, WI

This RV-6 completed in 1990 was the ninth aircraft built by Tony. He has since
built two more — an RV-6A and has just completed an RV-3. The distinctive insignia
on the tail represents the coat of arms of Lithuania — Tony's ancestral homeland.
An RV-4 was built prior to this RV-6, so Tony has completed every one of the
popular RV series aircraft.
Tony's first attempt at building aircraft started very early in life with a Knight
Twister, Flying Flea and a primary glider. His first completed aircraft, an Emeraude,
was started while in service stationed in Japan and finished later in Texas — as
were all subsequent aircraft built. These included in order: Flaglor Scooter, Volksplane, Turner T-40, a second Emeraude, Falco, and the four all-metal RV series
aircraft.

Dedicated to my wife, Morine

Acknowledgements

Over the last three decades I have been privileged to view, examine, and photograph thousands of homebuilt aircraft.

Today, homebuilts are a common sight and you might see them, not only at Oshkosh and at Sun 'n Fun in Florida but, also, at small town airports scattered across the U.S. and abroad.

I have had the privilege of talking to many builders. With justifiable pride, they have patiently explained to me the features I considered unique to their aircraft, and cheerfully answered my questions as well as those from the small crowds that invariably gather.

How could I possibly name all these fine folks who have contributed so much to this book?

Many of you builders, and your friends, too, may recognize some of the aircraft in the photos illustrating the text. My thanks to each and everyone of you. You are the ones who made it possible for me to pass on much of the vital information and details builders want.

This free exchange of knowledge is, indeed, essential to the life of the homebuilt movement.

A very special thanks, too, to the EAA for making its educational resources available to homebuilders everywhere. The EAA stands tall in promoting and guarding our precious homebuilt movement.

What Every Homebuilder Needs

Building your own airplane is one of the fastest growing and most popular activities in the world of general and sport aviation. Upon completion of your airplane, you experience a self-satisfaction and pride that makes all the long hours and hard work worthwhile. Through the homebuilt movement, new aircraft designs and innovations have provided important advancements for light aviation.

The Experimental Aircraft Association and its members have complied a tremendous amount of information that will help you with your aircraft building and restoration projects. Tony Bingelis has been a leader in developing and providing material that reaches out to all aspects of aircraft construction and maintenance.

This book on engines is one in a series of publications that Tony has authored to help you, the aircraft builder. Good luck with your project. Be sure to call on EAA whenever you need assistance.

Tom Poberezny

Tom Poberezny
President
Experimental Aircraft Association
EAA Aviation Foundation

CONTENTS

Other, more powerful Chevrolet, Ford auto engine conversions are also appearing more frequently and continue to titillate the interest of more and more builders.

Every year at Oshkosh and at Sun 'n Fun, we see all sorts of "new" engine developments and auto engine conversions. Each exhibitor expounds on the reliability and great progress being made — and earnestly tries to convince you it won't be long before their engine will be the engine of choice.

The competition includes, not only the more familiar names like VW, Rotax, Rotorway, Javelin Ford, GM, Geshwinder, Subaru, Hirth, Madza, but also a number of foreign entries like the interesting Canadian CAM100 and the exciting German Zoche Aero Diesel engines. The CAM100 is already appearing in homebuilts but to date, I have not seen one of the diesels fly.

Many of the older auto engine conversions are currently appearing in various homebuilt designs and, if you look carefully through the hundreds of show airplanes parked, you may see one for yourself.

Unfortunately, for the most part, though, you can't buy an auto conversion engine like you can a new Lycoming or a Continental. Instead, you will have to build one for yourself using many readily available components. However, in a few cases, very few indeed, you might be able to purchase a ready to fly engine.

This is somewhat discouraging for most builders because building the aircraft structure is time consuming enough.

On the other hand, if you have the time or can arrange to have an auto conversion built up for you for a reasonable cost, and your aircraft will be large enough to accommodate it, a good auto conversion would offer you still another engine option.

ENGINE MOUNT CONSIDERATIONS

The specific type and model aircraft engine you select will require a particular type shock mount installation. Ordinarily, the engine mount pads are cast into the engine crankcase and this installation proviso cannot be changed. You must, therefore, be prepared to obtain or fabricate the correct type of engine mount to accommodate that engine model.

In other words, some aircraft engines take simple **conical** shock mounts while others require a more complex **dynafocal** shock mount installation. As for converted auto engines, sometimes a different bed type engine shock mounting installation may have to be designed and custom built.

If you prefer a specific type of shock mount installation for an aircraft engine (dynafocal or conical), you will have to select one of the aircraft engine models that has the particular crankcase proviso you want.

This is an especially important decision for you kit builders who must, sooner or later, order a specific type engine mount with your kit.

Of course, once your kit and engine mount is ordered, you really won't have a choice. Your search for an engine will necessarily be limited to those models that will fit the selected engine mount type . . . conical or dynafocal.

As for the merits of one type of mount over the other, I doubt if you could tell what type of engine mount is under the cowl of any aircraft you happen to be flying in . . . unless you peeked beforehand.

Most everyone will agree, though, that a dynafocal mount results in what appears to be a smoother running engine — maybe because it cushions vibrations more effectively. Most everyone will also agree that the shock mounts for a dynafocal installation costs much, much more than the simple conical rubber shocks.

In the final analysis, if you came across a good low time conical mount engine that is reasonably priced, I certainly wouldn't hesitate getting it . . . provided, of course, the conical mount feature was your only reservation.

NEW VS. OVERHAULED

Sure, an overhauled engine will appear to be more attractively priced than one sporting a factory new list price tag. However, this assumption merits further discussion.

Of course, except for its very high cost, a factory new engine is the best choice. For one thing, every part in that engine will be new and the engine will have been test run at the factory. This means that you as a builder would not have to worry about test flying the engine.

On the other hand, a used engine that has just received a major overhaul and/or has newly chromed cylinders installed does require strict compliance with a very critical run-up and takeoff procedure.

Unfortunately, simultaneously testing a new airplane and a rebuilt engine that hasn't even been run in a test cell will create an increased risk and a serious operational dilemma for any builder.

My own first choice would be a new engine . . . if my finances would permit it.

The second choice would be a "low-to-mid-time" engine recently removed from an operational aircraft . . . and I would plan on using it without overhauling it provided everything checked out O.K.

BEGIN YOUR ENGINE SEARCH LOCALLY

Consider this. When you do locate an engine, you will want to examine it to see what you are getting. This inspection is far easier to accomplish locally than it would be for some engine located out of state hundreds of miles away.

Finding a suitable engine locally will reduce the number of potential problems normally encountered, not the least of which would be getting it home after you buy it (hopefully not sight unseen).

Buying a disassembled engine may be a big bargain . . . If you get all the parts. Advantage is that you will get a chance to check the crankshaft, camshaft, cylinders and other critical components for condition and wear.

Spread the word through your EAA Chapter members and the Chapter newsletter. Let them know you are in the market for an engine.

Visit all the nearby airports that have based aircraft and make a few inquiries. Be sure to leave your name, address and phone number. Ask if you can post your "engine wanted" information on their bulletin board.

Although advertising for an engine in local newspapers seldom produces results, it may be worth the try at least once or twice during construction. Remember, this engine search may be a long drawn out undertaking.

MOD SHOPS

Around the country there are a number of facilities that specialize in upgrading twin engined aircraft by installing larger, more powerful engines and making other changes in certificated aircraft. These places often remove engines and replace them with new higher horsepower powerplants.

The removed engines are usually high-time engines and sometimes may be purchased on the spot for the going price of a run-out engine.

Unfortunately, these sources are not as numerous or as active as they once were because the aviation economy is no longer as healthy as it once was. Then, too, some of these places are turning the engines back to the factory for the going core price.

STORM DAMAGED AIRCRAFT

Every year natural disasters strike around the country damaging aircraft as well as other properties. A wind or storm damaged aircraft could be a good buy

What a find! The builder obtained this mid-time engine when the owner decided he "needed" a new higher horsepower engine for his aircraft. Everything, firewall forward, baffles, accessories, etc. came with the engine . . . it was ready for flight.

just for the engine in it.

Typically, at the time of the disaster, the airplane was probably tied down, or hangared, and the engine was not running. It is, therefore, unlikely to have suffered any internal damage.

If the engine looks good externally, try to contact the owner, he might want to get rid of it immediately for whatever price he can get.

Ordinarily, you will have to cope with an insurance company in such a situation. Most of these have regular buyers who bid on all available wrecks.

However, it is well to remember that not all aircraft carry comprehensive (damage) insurance. Anyway, you would have better luck dealing with an individual.

At any rate, if you persevere you just might find a very good engine in what may be a badly bent airframe.

AIRCRAFT SALVAGE YARDS

Many aircraft salvage yards remove and sell aircraft engines on an "as is" basis. Prices will vary with the demand and availability of specific engine models, engine hours, and the quality of the engine logs . . . if any. If you have such a business activity within driving distance, it could become a possible source for an engine.

Try to get acquainted and pay them a visit from time to time.

It might help if you were to purchase some goodies for your project, occasionally. Some used items can be as good as new. For example, you will need a gascolator, cabin heat box, firewall grommets, an oil cooler, etc. do you get the drift?

ENGINE OVERHAUL SHOPS

There are many of these. Unfortunately, most of them will not sell an engine outright . . . you have to have one (a suitable core) in exchange. Sometimes,

however, outright sales are made.

Naturally, the outright sales price will be considerably higher than just the overhaul prices you see advertised.

SEARCH THROUGH AVIATION'S CLASSIFIEDS

Popular general aviation publications are good information sources for aviation products and services. However, not all of them are useful or effective for finding an engine. Among the more frequently referenced sources are:

SPORT AVIATION, EAA's major publication. It has a good specialized classified section.

KITPLANES magazine. It has a large classified section.

FLYER — formerly Western Flyer, now combined with General Aviation News. I believe it to be aviation's largest and best newspaper. It, too, has a large classified section.

TRADE-A-PLANE. This is strictly a classified advertising source for aircraft, engines, instruments, air-

Some automotive conversions can pose unique installation problems.

A different type of engine mount may be required if the engine you obtain is a base mounted auto conversion. Essentially, a hardwood bearer or large diameter tubing must first be fabricated. Then, engine mount tubing must be fitted and welded to complete a triangular self-bracing frame.

craft parts and aviation services. As such, it is the largest in the U.S.A., perhaps in the world.

It is also the average, homebuilder's favorite source. Most builders subscribe to the publication in anticipation that it will help them fill the unusual needs a builder develops during the construction of an airplane.

Since there are so many subscribers to TRADE-A-PLANE, competition for the "good deals" is keen. Bargains are usually snapped up as soon as the catalog-like yellow sheets come out.

That being the case, it would be wise to subscribe to the air mail edition and get the jump over the regular subscribers. This could be very important when you are seriously searching for an engine.

HOW ABOUT ADERTISING?

If you run an advertisement for an engine, you would expect to be the first and only one to learn of the availability of the engine. Unfortunately, as good an idea as this may sound, I find that people with engines to sell prefer to run their own ad, and seldom respond to "Engine Wanted" advertising.

There is a lot of competition out there from professional trades and buyers . . . and they are doing the same thing.

NEW ENGINES AT DISCOUNT PRICES?

Yes, there is such a thing as discounted factory new engines. The ultralight aircraft kit manufacturers led the way and usually sold their kits complete with two-cycle engines. And now, fortunately for many builders, this practice seems to be spreading . . . to the larger and faster experimental kit planes.

Builders of certain kit planes may now be afforded the opportunity of purchasing factory new engines for their kits at very attractive prices.

For example, Van's Aircraft, Inc., well known kit manufacturer of the popular all metal RV-3, RV-4, RV-6 and RV-6A series, has an OEM (Original Equipment Manufacturer) sales agreement with Lycoming. This permits Van's Aircraft to sell factory new Lycoming engines to his kit builders at a special reduced price. This represents a very real savings to the builder who wants to install a new engine.

Unfortunately, this deal is only for RV kit builders . . . and, as good a deal as this is, it still represents a price well beyond the reach of the average builder. This is understandable as the price of the discounted new engine is still far more costly than the complete aircraft kit . . . even with all the options.

Check with your kit manufacturer to see if they, too, have a similar arrangement with some engine manufacturer.

ABANDONED PROJECTS

Be on the lookout for abandoned projects. These sometimes prove to be an unexpected source for an engine. The builder may have already acquired an engine and is offering it as part of the deal.

Often a builder will be willing to sell the engine separately. On the other hand, it might even be worth it to buy his entire project simply to get the engine.

You could, then, advertise and sell off what you don't want to keep. This is how I got the engine for my last RV-6 project.

As for selling off the parts you don't want to keep, don't worry about that — all you need is one buyer. Although you're looking for an engine, somebody else may be just as eagerly looking for parts.

A FEW WORDS OF CAUTION

Many of the engines advertised for sale may have been removed from operational or cracked up aircraft weeks, months, sometimes, years ago.

You have to realize that the particular engine you have located may not have been properly pickled. If so, and a long time has passed since it was last operated, you should consider the possibility that its cylinder walls and camshaft may have begun to rust.

The carburetor of an engine that has not been operated for a long time will have dried out and its gaskets may all have to be replaced before operating the engine. For that matter, the engine should receive careful attention before operating it if you don't intend to overhaul it.

One final word of caution. Don't buy an engine that has no data plate. It may have been assembled from junked parts and never did have a serial number . . . or it may be a stolen engine.

Anyhow, getting a new data plate from the engine manufacturer is impossible without a letter of approval from the FAA. The FAA will want to know what happened to the original data plate.

ADDITIONAL READING

My book, FIREWALL FORWARD, page 34, "Locating A Suitable Engine".

Don't wait until you have come this far before you begin to look for an engine.

What Engine?
Bigger is Not Always Better

IS BIGGER BETTER? Does a more powerful engine always improve the airplane? . . . any airplane? Which engine would be the "best one" for your project? What are your options?

You should explore these as well as quite a few other questions before you finalize your own specifications and plunk down a lot of money for an engine that may not fit your needs.

Because engine availability, at any given time, is so unpredictable, it is never too early in a project to start thinking about your engine requirements. Such a determination is an especially important one because a good engine will gobble up approximately 1/3 of the total cost of your project.

ARE YOU SURE YOU'LL NEED AN ENGINE?

An engine is a major expenditure and it is one that should not be rushed into until you are absolutely, positively sure you will be needing an engine in the first place. Here is what I mean.

As most of you know, an airplane project, traditionally, begins with the construction of the tail surfaces. This is logical because in doing so you will have ample time to become thoroughly acquainted with the type of construction you will be using to build the wings and the rest of the airplane.

Successfully completing the tail surfaces could be ample proof of your determination and stick-to-it-iveness . . . but will you be able to persevere until you bring to completion what may well be the longest project you ever attempted?

Since tail surfaces ordinarily represent but a relatively modest cash investment, this first stage of construction can be considered to be a shakedown period. During this time, any disenchanted builder could elect to abandon his project, should he make that decision . . . and a number of builders do just that, citing some very compelling reasons for doing so. Have any of these ever crossed your mind?

"I found the design was not what I really expected it to be and I am no longer interested in it."

"I really can't spare the time for building an airplane."

"I found that I lack the patience to develop my skills (much less learn new ones) for building an (all-metal/composite/wood or tube and fabric - pick one) airplane."

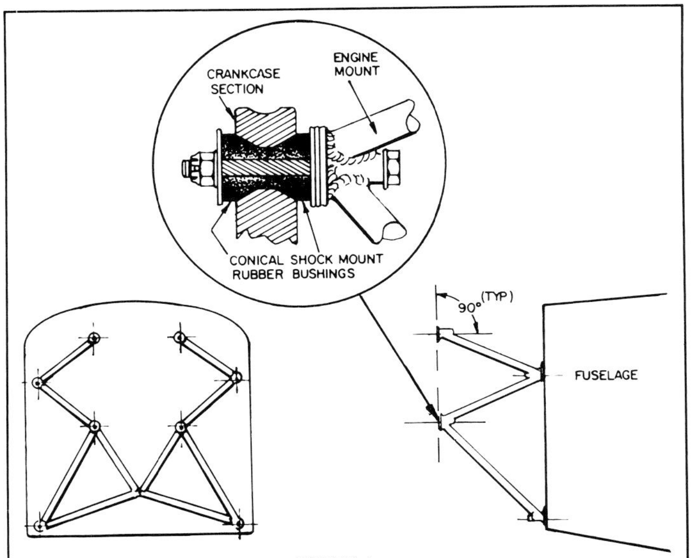

![Figure 1 and Figure 2 engine mount diagrams]

FIGURE I.
THE CONICAL MOUNT
(TYPICAL)

FRONT VIEW   SIDE VIEW

CRANKCASE SECTION   ENGINE MOUNT
CONICAL SHOCK MOUNT RUBBER BUSHINGS
90°(TYP)
FUSELAGE

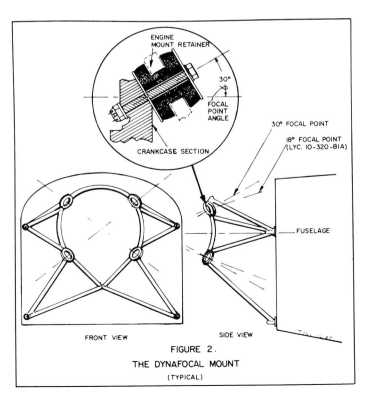

FIGURE 2.
THE DYNAFOCAL MOUNT
(TYPICAL)

FRONT VIEW   SIDE VIEW

ENGINE MOUNT RETAINER
30°
FOCAL POINT ANGLE
CRANKCASE SECTION
30° FOCAL POINT
18° FOCAL POINT (LYC. IO-320-BIA)
FUSELAGE

"Building from 'scratch' involves too much work and takes too long. Besides, I can't afford the cost of a kit project . . . not without depriving my family of the little luxuries they deserve."

"My wife told me, 'Either that airplane goes or I go'."

And so it goes.

WHAT'S YOUR OWN VERDICT?

I'll bet most of us can cite more reasons and excuses for giving up a project than anyone else can possibly dream up for continuing one. Unfortunately, it is a situation some of us might have to face someday.

Terminating a project is never an easy decision to make but, in the long run, for some builders at any rate it might be in the best interest of all concerned to do so if the slightest doubt about continuing a project exists.

Cheer up . . . if your workmanship has been adequate, and you do feel compelled to abandon the project, you can always sell it and your special tools to recoup some of the costs. Then, with a clear conscience you can charge the rest off to education and recreation.

But more likely you ARE enjoying the project and are satisfied that your work is structurally sound. Not only that, you are probably just as eager to continue as most builders are at this stage — and you would NEVER entertain the idea of giving up your project.

With that somber discourse out of the way, let's square off and face that next big decision you will have to make sooner or later, namely determining which engine you think you want for your airplane.

This, too, is a difficult determination to make because of the large number of options you and you alone control.

WHAT DOES THE DESIGNER RECOMMEND?

Each aircraft design is developed around certain en-

Photo 1 - Notice how close to the wing that heavy low power Model A Ford engine had to be mounted to obtain a manageable CG location in the old Pietenpol design.

Photo 2 - In contrast, note how the fuselage and engine mount has to be extended in the Pietenpols fitted with the lighter aircraft engines.

gine options. A good clue as to the engine best suited for your project might be ascertained from the engine the designer installed in his prototype. In addition, his literature will undoubtedly stipulate the horsepower range the aircraft was designed to safely accommodate.

Some builders are bad about ignoring the designer's horsepower limitations and often go ahead on their own and install a much larger engine — with or without the designer's approval — hoping to achieve superior performance.

This can be a dangerous thing to do. Why? I'll try to tell you why by citing a few worst case scenarios as examples.

It is unlikely that your aircraft's structure was designed to handle engines much heavier and more powerful than those few recommended.

Anyone building from a kit quickly learns that any small modification you make seems to compound problems and affect other parts. For instance, if you elect to install a larger engine you will find that the furnished cowling will not fit it without major surgery. The exhaust system, too, may have to be modified.

Be advised that engines more powerful than those specified by the designer will produce higher thrust and torque loads than those the structure was designed to handle safely. To avoid exceeding the gross weight and G loads specified, such an engine should be derated with mechanical control stops.

In addition, substituting a heavier engine will upset the design weight and balance calculations, and may force you to reduce or eliminate the baggage allowance. Furthermore, you might have to redesign and build a shorter engine mount . . . and maybe add ballast (that's dead weight, son). Carrying this line of thinking further, a larger more powerful engine will require a larger propeller. To accommodate that increased propeller diameter, longer landing gear legs may have to be built in order to assure a safe ground clearance for the propeller.

And that is not all. A more powerful engine will ordinarily cost more, initially, and will gulp down more fuel. Therefore, unless you also increase the aircraft's fuel capacity somehow, the aircraft's flight duration will be definitely reduced.

Increasing the fuel capacity can solve that problem but creates another. You will be adding still more structural and fuel weight. Consequently, although the aircraft's range may be increased with the added fuel capacity, the overall performance may suffer because your payload will be reduced and/or your gross weight will be increased beyond its design limit.

Here's still another glitch. Although an increase in horsepower generally produces a shorter take-off, and a better climb, don't think for a minute that the attendant increase in top speed will be something phenomenal. It won't be. The reason, of course, is well known. Doubling the horsepower will not double the top

speed . . . far from it. The boost in top speed is often disappointing and seldom does a builder see anything over a 25% increase . . . and that would be with the fuel flowing through the engine like a stream of water flushing down the toilet.

Consider this observation for the overkill. Most of the more powerful engines are high compression engines and have to be fed that expensive 100 octane low lead aircraft fuel. That means you may not be able to use auto fuel in your airplane . . . and you know what that will do for your fuel costs when you are burning over 10 gph.

A WORD ABOUT ENGINE MOUNTS

Some builders have the mistaken idea that they can elect to use either a conical mount or a dynafocal mount with the engine they acquire. This is not true. The engine you get can only take one kind of a shock mount, no matter what your personal preference may be.

If you are a kit builder, you will have to decide which type of engine mount to order with your kit. If, for example, you specify the conical mount, then your engine search will have to be limited to those engines designed to take a conical mount. Or, in other words, if you already have an engine, order the mount to fit it. Otherwise, select the mount type (dynafocal or conical) you want, and look for an engine to fit the mount.

A dynafocal mount is considered to be the superior type of shock mount. Its large rubber discs cushion engine vibrations better than do the smaller cone shaped rubbers of a conical mount.

However, don't assume that a conical mount is something to avoid. Far from it. Anyway, I doubt if most pilots can tell what kind of engine shock mount is installed in the particular airplane they happen to be flying at the time.

A conical engine mount is much simpler and easier to fabricate than a dynafocal mount. Furthermore, the conical mount's cone shaped shocks are very inexpensive and cost only a few bucks for a complete set of eight. By comparison, a set of dynafocal shocks will cost well over $150.

So, if the flat areas of the rear crankcase of the engine you obtain, or already have, has horizontally drilled bolt holes with large countersinks for mounting the engine, it is a conical mount engine.

Dynafocal engine mounts are much more difficult to design and to build because the engine mount must be built around a precisely preformed dynafocal ring that has correctly slanted attach points already built in. The focal point for each of the four slanted engine mount bolts is projected, for most Lycoming O-320 engines, to intersect at some point inside the engine forming an imaginary 30 degree angle to the engine's centerline.

NOTE: A word of caution. The Lycoming IO-320-B1A, as used in Twin Comanches, was designed with a focal point of 18 (not 30) degrees and is designated as a Type 2 dynafocal mount. Furthermore, the machined slanted rear crankcase mounting surfaces have recessed notches that require the use of aluminum spacers to provide crankcase clearance for the dynafocal shocks. Keep this in mind if you intend to build or have an engine mount built for an IO-320-B1A Lycoming engine.

PLANNING TO USE A CONSTANT SPEED PROPELLER?

A new fixed pitch non-certified ("homebuilt") wood propeller may be obtained for approximately $500.

A fixed pitch certified metal prop will cost, roughly, $2000 new. Unfortunately though, most high performance homebuilts, using engines of 150-180 hp, require propellers having a much higher pitch than those available for commercially produced aircraft. You would, therefore, have to buy a metal propeller and have it repitched . . . if you can find a propeller shop willing to work on an experimental propeller.

Constant speed propellers (Hamilton, etc.) cost approximately $3000 to $5000, depending on your source.

In addition to the high price tag for a controllable propeller, there are also other negative aspects. In the first place, the engine you expect to use with a controllable prop must:

1. Have a hollow crankshaft . . . unless you intend to use an electric propeller or some other propeller control system.

2. Have provision for a propeller governor.

If the engine can meet both of those requirements it can accommodate a standard constant speed propeller . . . but be prepared to cope with the extra weight. That propeller, with its governor installed, will weigh around 60 pounds. (Fixed pitch wood props weigh less than 20.) So, as is the case with a larger engine, you will be confronted with an increase in the aircaft's empty weight, and a new weight and balance problem.

The relatively few homebuilts flying with the more powerful auto engine conversions are most likely to be found installed in biplanes and in larger aircraft with wing areas that can handle the extra weight.

Letting it all hang out might be O.K. for this old Pietenpol, but that concept is unacceptable for a high performance modern design. However, tightly fitted cowlings make it very difficult to locate the large radiator effectively.

The Geshwinder Ford's massive belt drive effectively provides the necessary rpm reduction . . . an important accessory for the fast turning auto engines.

ABOUT AUTO ENGINE CONVERSIONS

Except for the perky little VW conversions, the more powerful auto engine conversions (130-180 hp) are still a rarity on the average airport.

Someday when you see three or more airplanes of the same type equipped with the same kind of auto engine conversion parked side-by-side, you will know that auto conversions have arrived and are becoming a serious alternative to the somewhat stodgier aircraft engine. However, that day is not yet close at hand.

A new 150 hp aircraft engine (Lycoming) does cost more than a custom built new auto conversion of similar power. However, the aircraft engine is a certificated engine with a proven track record. Your new auto conversion will carry no such assurance, and it will be strictly experimental in the literal sense of the word. This is especially true when it is built up by a non-expert engine mechanic with a limited number of precision tools at his disposal.

On the other hand, a good used aircraft engine will cost less than a new auto conversion and yet that older, mid-time aircraft engine can be expected to accumulate more hours than the auto conversion before it will have to be overhauled.

For example, I understand that the reduction unit alone can cost about $2600 for a 6 cylinder auto conversion. Then, there are other costs you must absorb in addition to the cost of a new or low mileage basic engine core. Some of the build-up costs include but, naturally, are by no means limited to a radiator, hoses, carburetor, starter, ignition system, special hardware and machine shop work. Add these items all together and I'm afraid the costs could approach the cost of a newly overhauled aircraft engine.

So far nothing has been said about an auto engine's biggest drawback — WEIGHT. Weight for the power produced.

Because the auto engine conversions (Ford/Chevrolet/Oldsmobile, etc.) make bulkier and heavier installations than most comparable aircraft engines, they cannot be readily squeezed into the average homebuilts.

In general, you can figure that an auto engine conversion will weigh approximately 50-75 pounds more than an aircraft engine of similar power (125 hp to 200 hp range). Some of the weight claims made for the auto engine conversions may fail to include the weight of the radiator, coolant, hoses and sometimes an accessory or two.

What counts is the all-inclusive flying weight of the installation . . . and that generally will be significantly heavier than an ordinary aircraft engine.

As a result, the few homebuilts flying with an auto engine conversion on board are usually found in bi-

Radial engines are large and look better on antiques and large homebuilt biplanes. This would look funny on a VariEze.

23

Hundreds of small homebuilts are powered by various VW conversions. However, it is doubtful that many of them are using a propeller this small.

The small Canadian CAM100 engine is growing in popularity and is beginning to make its appearance as more homebuilts are completed with this installation.

planes and in designs with larger wing areas . . . say, over 100 sq. ft.

Many years ago, way back in the early 1930s, Model A auto engines were being installed in Pietenpols. Later, Corvair conversions were also tried in the venerable aircraft. Both of these engines were comparatively heavy for the power produced. However, the installations were fairly practical because the Pietenpol had a rather large wing area and the slow turning engine swinging a large diameter prop was positioned close to the wing.

You probably have noticed that the newer Pietenpols, using the lighter aircraft engines, have had their fuselages and engine mounts extended for weight and balance reasons to compensate for the absence of the original heavier engines.

Conversely, replacing a light VW or Rotax type engine with a heavier aircraft engine of similar power is also a potential trip for the builder.

Many builders still distrust the VW's and the efficient 2 cycle engines and try, instead, to squeeze a typically larger and heavier 65 hp or 85 hp aircraft engine into what generally happens to be a very small engine compartment space.

This, of course, has a drastic effect on the weight and balance if not handled properly and, of course, requires drastic cowling modification to enclose the bulkier aircraft engine. Examples I have in mind are the attempts to re-engine Sonerais, Dragonflys, Quickies, PL-4s and similar small sport planes.

PROOF OF THE PUDDING

Year after year the annual CAFE 400 efficiency runs prove that the aircraft with the bigger engines are not necessarily the fastest and most efficient.

ENGINE INSTALLATION 2

Engine Hook-Up Tips

Most of your bolt-on engine accessories and parts should be installed before hanging the engine. Access, now that the engine is bolted to the mount and firewall, will be quite restricted.

Check to see how much clearance you actually have between the engine accessories and the firewall. For example, check the space between the firewall and the magnetos. Also, if a propeller governor is installed, check the space between it and the firewall.

If there isn't much room there, you will have to accept the fact that sometime in the future the engine will have to be pulled off its mount before the magnetos can be removed. But worse than that, you may find that you will have to cut a recess into the firewall to provide the space needed for the installation of the ignition harness. The same problem may affect the propeller governor control mechanism when a governor is mounted on the rear accessory case.

If the firewall clearances present no problem, you are ready to begin hooking up and installing the works. The big items will include the ignition system, fuel and oil systems, exhaust system, engine controls, wiring, and the installation of fittings and connections for the engine monitoring instruments . . . to mention a few of the more important tasks ahead.

Obviously, covering all these subjects — and more — in detail would be impossible in the short space available here. Actually, I could write a book on the individual subjects . . . as a matter of fact, I did. My innate modesty notwithstanding, I seriously recommend that, if you have yet to install an engine in your project, you acquire a copy of my book, "FIREWALL FORWARD". It contains much more information on engine installations for homebuilts. (Order from EAA - 1-800/843-3612).

Well, that may be O.K. for later, but just where would be a good place for you to begin right now?

I guess there really is no single best starting place for making the engine hook-ups. Much, of course, will depend on the complexity of your aircraft.

However, even a simple engine installation with no electrical system will entail plenty of work by the time you complete the fuel connections to the carburetor, hook up the throttle and carburetor controls, and connect the ignition harness correctly. Naturally, all engine installations, even simple ones, must be fitted with the mandatory minimum VFR instrumentation listed in the Federal Aviation Regulations (FAR Part 91). Included in that list are the three engine monitoring instruments, namely, the oil pressure gauge, the oil temperature gauge (a water temperature gauge for liquid cooled engines), and the tachometer. Let's start with the most logical things to be done first.

ESTABLISHING THE AIRCRAFT GROUND

Without a doubt, your first engine hook-up should be the grounding of the engine to the engine mount, and to the aircraft. Remember, your engine is insulated (electrically) from the engine mount and the rest of the aircraft by rubber shocks.

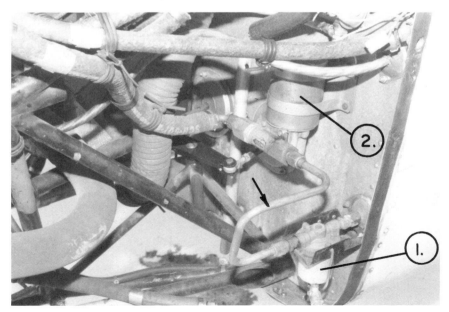

An exception to the rule. Using a rigid aluminum fuel line inside the engine compartment is O.K. in this instance. Both the gascolator (1), and the aux. pump (2), are rigidly attached to the firewall, and there is no movement between the two.

An excellent aircraft electrical ground is virtually guaranteed by connecting a short, fairly heavy, flexible grounding strap (or a stranded AWG No. 8 cable fitted with terminal connectors) between the engine and the engine mount.

Careful . . . the ordinary fine wire low capacity electrical bonding jumper straps generally used for aircraft bonding are not heavy enough and should not be used for this purpose.

The aircraft grounding connections should always be made with nuts and bolts . . . never with rivets.

Secure one end of the ground strap to most any nearby engine bolt, and the other terminal to a welded tab on the engine mount or some other solid point.

NOTE: Never install any kind of bracket or aluminum connector under any of the engine's cylinder base hold-down nuts.

Some builders like to install two grounding straps — one on each side of the engine.

In wood and composite aircraft, a special effort must be made to ground the instrument panel to provide a convenient aircraft ground for the wiring to be completed inside the aircraft.

If your airplane has an aft mounted battery and the aircraft frame is wood or composite, you should run the battery ground cable (same size as the power cable) all the way forward through the firewall and connect it directly to the engine. Normally, a No. 4 insulated stranded copper cable is heavy enough for most homebuilts. A lot of builders use a stranded No. 4 electric welder cable because it is priced right and is readily available at most welding supply sources. Commercially produced aircraft often use a heavier No. 1 cable.

NEXT, THE IGNITION SYSTEM

Unless your magnetos are of the internal grounding type, they will be hot until you hook up the "P" leads (ground wires).

Although you may not yet have fuel in the tanks, play it safe. Do not install the propeller until the magnetos are properly connected and grounded by an ignition switch (Figure 1).

The magneto circuit is simple. All you need to do is run a single wire from each magneto to an ignition switch of some sort . . . even a toggle switch, if you prefer. The wire size requirement is small and a No. 18 shielded wire is adequate.

If no radio is to be on board, the magneto ground wire ("P" lead) need not be a shielded wire. However, the way the FAA is cranking out new governmental mandates, I would even be tempted to install shielded magneto wires in an aerial "putt-putt" — just in case.

You might also consider installing an individual magneto filter on each magneto to eliminate ignition noise. On the other hand, expending about $35 for two magneto filters might not be necessary. The shielded spark plugs and ignition harness, backed up by the shielded magneto "P" leads, may be all you need for noise-free radio reception. Anyway, you can always retrofit the filters later as they simply connect to the "P" leads at the magnetos.

Before you go any further . . . if you haven't already installed the engine cooling baffles, maybe you had better take on that job next. One reason for this is that your ignition harness will have to be routed through the back baffles. Furthermore, the proposed location for the oil cooler may also require the presence of the engine cooling baffles before it can be installed.

SOME THOUGHTS ABOUT ENGINE CONTROLS

You can proceed with your other engine hook-ups in any sequence you find convenient.

I like to work from the inside areas out. That is, I generally find it easier to install the engine controls to the carburetor before access there becomes more difficult with the installation of the exhaust pipes, heat muff, mufflers, fuel and oil cooler lines, ducting, etc.

Here is something else to consider. Your planned hook-up sequencing may have to be altered when you find that you don't have all the controls, hose fittings, wires, nuts and bolts needed to complete a particular installation. This happens more often than not. But don't let that deter you. Simply proceed to some other hook-up you can complete working with the parts you already have on hand. After all, everything will have to be installed before you operate the engine.

Unless you have a computer memory, it would be a good idea to start a "need-to-get list" so you won't forget to order those hardware parts you didn't know you would need.

In the interest of safety, discipline yourself to complete securing both ends of each assembly and each circuit before leaving it for some other task. Believe me, it is so easy to overlook replacing that incorrect nut, or safetying that part sometime later. The "I'll get back to the later" mentality is a bum habit to develop.

What kind of throttle do you want? Decide whether you want a fighter-type left side throttle quadrant, or would be willing to settle for a simple push-pull throttle knob with a thumb operated knurled friction lock. Your parts requirements are different for each type.

In a side-by-side two seater, the preferred throttle location would be in the vicinity of the lower panel center. In that location it would also be accessible from the right seat.

Installing a lever type throttle will always result in a heavier, more complex, installation as you will have to fabricate a bellcrank or two and possibly have to devise and install a torque tube assembly on the firewall. Usually, this is necessary to reverse the throttle lever action so that shoving the throttle lever full forward will cause the carburetor throttle arm to move to the wide open position. another problem associated with lever type engine controls is the need to obtain the correct length flexible controls with threaded ends. I do not recommend using a throttle control that terminates

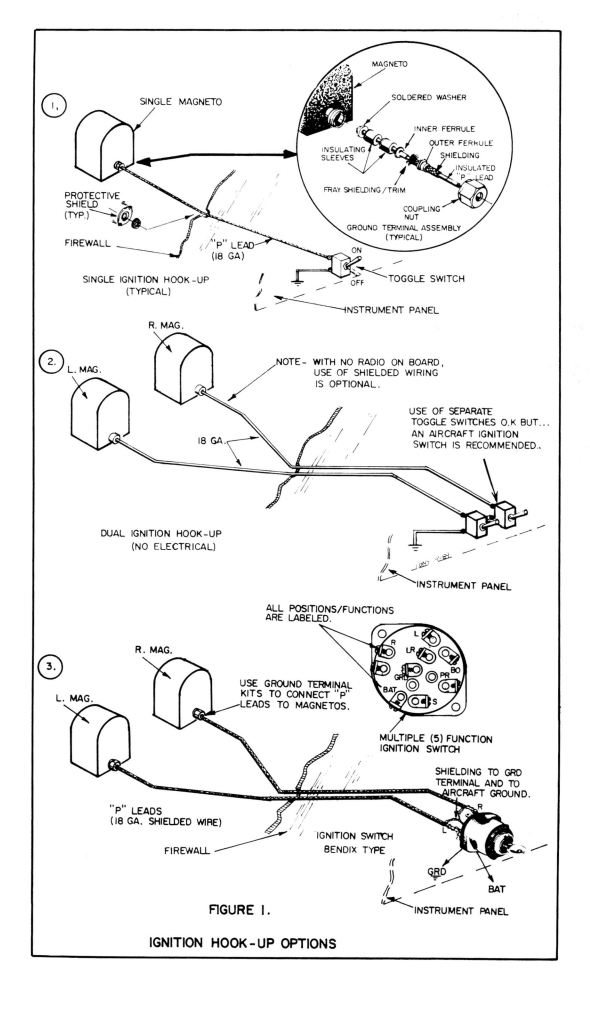

FIGURE I.

IGNITION HOOK-UP OPTIONS

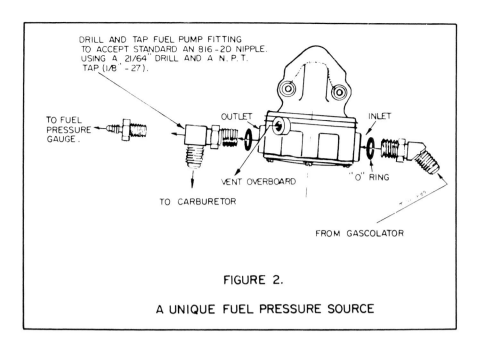

DRILL AND TAP FUEL PUMP FITTING
TO ACCEPT STANDARD AN 816-2D NIPPLE.
USING A 21/64" DRILL AND A N.P.T.
TAP (1/8" - 27).

TO FUEL
PRESSURE
GAUGE.

OUTLET

INLET

VENT OVERBOARD

"O" RING

TO CARBURETOR

FROM GASCOLATOR

FIGURE 2.

A UNIQUE FUEL PRESSURE SOURCE

in a bent wire arrangement — no matter how it is secured.

And I certainly do not recommend using a vernier type throttle knob. They are ideal for the mixture control and prop control, but entail too great a risk when using one for the throttle. The risk? You might forget to mash the center button when you suddenly decide you need full power. That vernier throttle won't budge unless you first depress that center button. Forgetting to do so in an emergency situation is very possible . . . and very dangerous.

Since the carburetor is situated under the engine on the aircraft's centerline, you should have saved a clear area in the lower central portion of the firewall to afford the most direct routing for the throttle and mixture control.

Unfortunately, it is most unlikely that you will find a convenient nearby component or bracket to which you can clamp the throttle and mixture control shaft housings. Since this problem also effects the installa-

tion of the propeller governor control, you may be forced to construct a special bracket for it also.

Although most builders ultimately manage to secure their engine control housings to a fairly rigid bracket, and at the proper distance from the carburetor levers, sometimes an otherwise good installation is jeopardized by using rubber cushioned clamps to immobilize the throttle and mixture control housings.

This is a poor way to do it because the cushioned material is not generally fuel resistant, and when it becomes oil soaked (and it will) may allow the control housing to slip. Just think how embarrassing it would be to push in the throttle and have nothing happen.

Always use metal to metal clamping to immobilize your controls and bowden cable housings at the appropriate distance from the carburetor levers. It is the safer way to do it.

Make sure the carburetor lever moves to the wide open position when the throttle is pushed forward.

The mixture control, likewise, must cause the car-

These low profile Cessna type cabin heat valve assemblies are a hot selling item at Oshkosh and Sun 'n Fun Fly Markets.

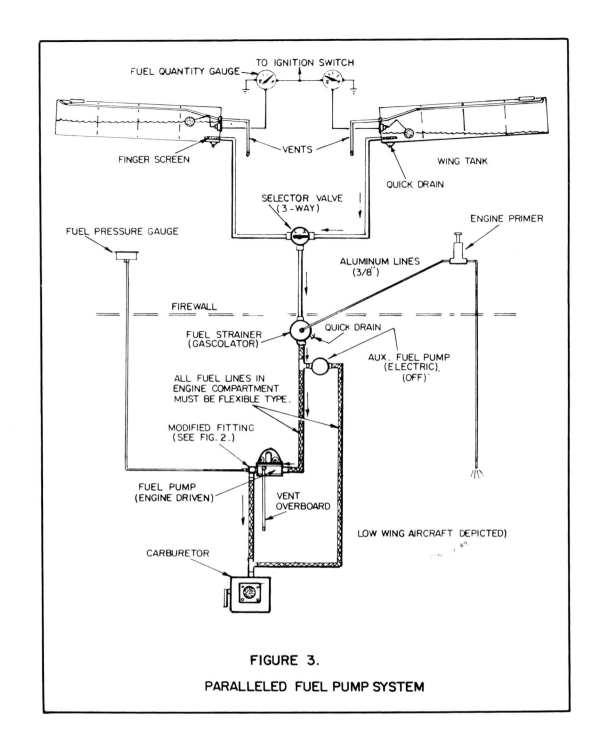

FIGURE 3.

PARALLELED FUEL PUMP SYSTEM

buretor lever to move to the rich position when moved forward.

Both controls — actually, all engine controls — should have a little bit of spring-back when moved to the full forward position in order to ensure getting maximum travel and output.

The positive way to verify this is by having someone move the controls in the cockpit, at your command, while you look for the proper movement at the engine. There should be no binding or rubbing throughout the travel limits of any engine control . . . nor should there be the slightest flexing at the point where the flexible control housings are clamped.

Don't forget to make provisions for carburetor heat. Use the red (SCAT) high temperature resistant ducting to conduct the hot air from the heat muff to the carburetor. Although all carburetor equipped engines must have carburetor heat, fuel injected engines seldom have a like arrangement or requirement.

One more reminder, try to obtain the correct length for each of the flexible engine controls. Extra long lengths are difficult to accommodate without introducing an excessive number of bends and increased friction in the control's operation.

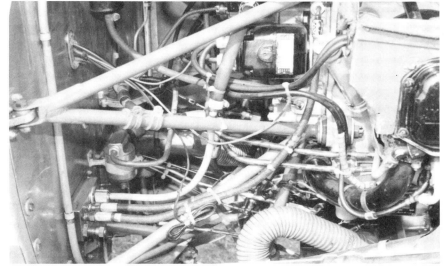

This proves that beauty is only skin deep. Remove the cowling and what do you see? A heterogeneous agglomeration best described as engine compartment clutter.

A VariEze Cont. O-200 engine installation well under way. Note the engine breather fitting (1), and the spiral wrapped door springs to increase radiated heat in the carburetor heat muff being assembled (2). The short filler neck (3), may pose problems later when checking or adding oil.

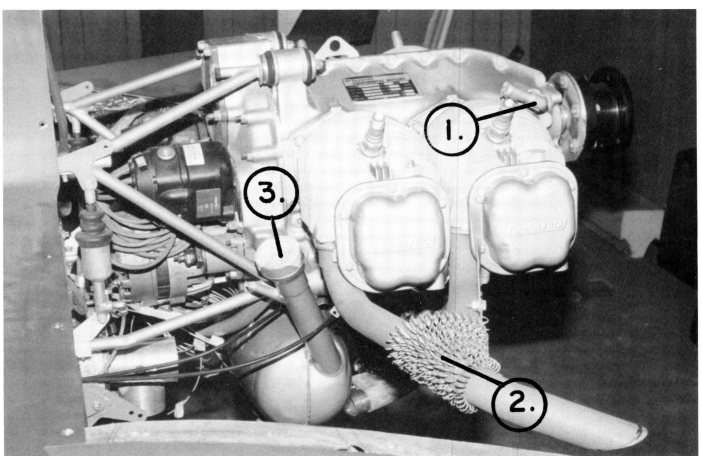

THE ALL IMPORTANT FUEL SYSTEM

Know what type of fitting is required for each assembly. For example, you cannot safely screw a straight threaded flared fitting into a pipe thread.

Although most components for light aircraft are tapped for a 1/8" pipe thread, don't assume this is always so. There are exceptions. The later style engine driven fuel pumps now have straight threads which require the installation of an "O" ring with the fitting so that it will seal properly.

The rule . . . check it out and be positive that the fitting you are trying to screw in is the correct one. A fuel leak can result in an engine failure or fire.

Be sure to use the correct 37 degree flaring tool to fabricate your aluminum lines. The automotive 45 degree flaring tool must not be used for aircraft fittings.

The minimum recommended diameter for an aluminum fuel line (5052-O aluminum preferred) is 3/8" O.D. with a .035" wall thickness. For a flexible (rubber) fuel line this translates to a -6 size which has a 3/8" inside diameter.

The rigid aluminum lines may be used anywhere inside the aircraft up to the firewall. From the firewall to the engine, however, all lines must be fabricated with flexible hoses.

Because the engine is hung on shock mounts, there will always be a lot of movement between it and the airframe. Obviously, a rigid fuel line would soon break.

Carefully route your fuel lines so that there are no low places in them between connections. That is, try to run each fuel line in a constantly rising, or descending, slope.

1. Between the fuel tank and the fuel selector valve.

2. Between the fuel selector and the gascolator.

3. Between the gascolator and the electric fuel pump.

4. Between the electric aux pump and the engine driven fuel pump or

5. Between the engine pump and the carburetor.

Do you get the idea that this is an important factor?

Keep your fuel lines away from the hot exhaust pipes.

It is difficult, sometimes, to find the correct type fittings — especially when trying to plumb a paralleled fuel pump system (Figure 3). I notice that in some Pipers a heavy plain ol' grey iron "T" fitting is used at the carburetor. It looks like it might have come straight from the plumbing section of a hardware store . . . 'nuff said.

THE ELECTRICAL STUFF

Select a wiring diagram you like and follow it.

The major things to remember are to use cables large enough for the loads expected, and to be sure to install shielded wires wherever needed.

Here's an example. The starter is a heavy current user and the cable connecting it to the starter solenoid should be at least a No. 4, possibly a No. 1, size cable. It need not be shielded as the starter circuit is inoperative in flight and will pose no radio interference problem.

On the other hand, the wires from the alternator do need to be shielded cables. A No. 12 or even a No. 14 shielded cable from the alternator "F" terminal to the voltage regulator "F" terminal should suffice. A heavier shielded cable (No. 10) should be installed between the alternator "B" terminal and the main engine circuit breaker at the bus bar.

At best, the typical engine compartment is a confused mess to view — makes me wonder if anybody could ever make the heterogeneous agglomeration look neat and orderly.

To help reduce this "offensive to the eye" engine compartment clutter, try bundling the wiring wherever practical. This means you may have to resist that weight saving impulse to make your wires as short as possible because that will only make your bundling efforts rather ineffective.

A FEW MORE OBSERVATIONS

The Lycomings have a 3/4" oil breather outlet while the small 4 cylinder Continentals are fitted with a 5/8" outlet. In either case, use the correct size hose and do not attempt to step down the I.D. to a smaller size.

It's very much the same thing with the oil coolers installed on Lycomings. Use the correct fittings to accommodate the preferred -8 size hose.

And, finally, I would like to emphasize that a new homebuilt is entitled to new oil and fuel hoses even if you have to assemble them yourself.

Fuel injected Continental IO-240 shown here is installed in a Tri-R KIS.

```
┌─────────────────────────────────────────────────────────┐
│                 USEFUL TORQUE VALUES                     │
│                (For Engine Installations)                │
│                                                          │
│  BASIC RULE:  Always use manufacturer's torque values.   │
│                   (When available)                       │
│                                                          │
│  1. General torque values for nuts and capscrews.        │
│       *1/2"    nuts/cap screws -    500 inch lbs.        │
│       *7/16"   nuts/cap screws -    400 inch lbs.        │
│       *3/8"    nuts/cap screws -    300 inch lbs.        │
│       *5/16"   nuts/cap screws -    150 inch lbs.        │
│       *1/4"    nuts/cap screws -     75 inch lbs.        │
│                                                          │
│  2. Specific Applications                                │
│     *Exhaust stack to cylinder attach nuts - 160-180 inch lbs.│
│     *Oil Filter Bolt (3/4" -16) AC can type - 300 inch lbs.│
│             (Caution - Do not over tighten)              │
│     *Spark Plugs - 360-420 inch lbs.                     │
│     *Hose Clamps - (worm type, stainless steel) - 20 inch lbs.│
│                      Figure 3                            │
└─────────────────────────────────────────────────────────┘
```

• Vacuum pump/regulator/fittings.

The following firewall mounted components (these may be mounted inside or outside the firewall):

• Battery solenoid.
• Over-voltage regulator.
• Starter solenoid.
• Voltage regulator.

DO IT YOURSELF ITEMS

In addition to all of the foregoing, you will have to devise and fabricate your own brackets to support and clamp the individual control housings for the operation of the throttle, mixture and propeller controls. This is necessary to ensure that these controls can be properly positioned and connected to the carburetor to ensure their positive and smooth operation.

Also essential is the fabrication of supports for the exhaust tail pipes. Properly installed tail pipe braces will help ensure a longer life for your exhaust system.

These braces can be made of 3/8" dia. steel tubing heated and flattened at both ends. The ends can be drilled for AN3 bolts and bent to whatever angle is needed. Bolt one end to a convenient crankcase bolt and clamp and bolt the other end to the exhaust pipe.

Don't bolt support braces rigidly to the engine mount or fuselage structure because the movement of the engine in its shock mounts may cause the braces and exhausts to crack and fail. Failed exhaust stacks seem to be the most prevalent mechanical failure homebuilders endure.

Oh, yes, install short blast tubes in the rear engine baffle to blow air over both magnetos to keep them cool.

And, finally, don't forget the "miscellaneous stuff". I never seem to have enough hardware items for the job . . . you know, washers, nuts, hose clamps, terminals, tie wraps, etc., etc.

If I overlooked doing or installing anything, you can rest assured that my next homebuilder visitor will let me know.

"Measure twice and cut once."

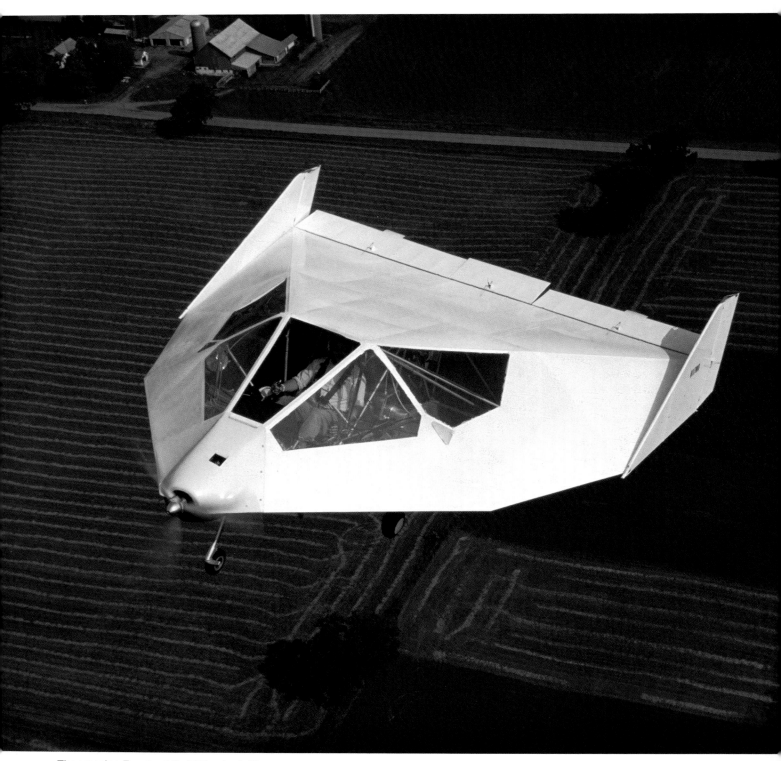

The amazing Facetmobile "lifting body" is powered by a 50 hp Rotax 503 2-cycle engine turning a 3-blade, ground adjustable GSC prop. Single place, the 19.5 ft. long, 15 ft. wide Facetmobile has a total lifting area of over 200 square feet and an empty weight of only 370 lbs.

FIREWALL PREPARATION ■3■

How to Make
Firewall Grommet Shields

Ever since the publication of my book, **Firewall Forward,** in 1983, I have been receiving countless queries asking for possible sources for the firewall shields/grommets illustrated on pages 64 and 66. It seems that most builders would prefer using those neat little rascals instead of sealing the firewall with a rubber grommet and some messy sealant.

Because of the difficulty builders experience in sealing the firewall, I can understand why most builders like to use bulkhead fittings wherever they can as the preferred way to pass plumbing through the firewall. Properly installed, bulkhead fittings do not need any further protection or form of sealant.

Unfortunately, bulkhead fittings cannot be used everywhere so builders continue to seal firewall openings with rubber grommets and dabs of silicone adhesive "frosting" around the wires, cables or controls passing through the firewall. This "better than nothing" solution usually results in a messy appearance. Besides, the treatment is not fire resistant — far from it.

More recently, a high temperature red silicone adhesive has become commonly available at auto parts stores. Although it is capable of withstanding temperatures of 500 to 600 degrees F., it, too, falls short of preventing flame penetration for any length of time.

You should realize that your firewall is supposed to act as a flame barrier between the engine compartment and you in the cockpit. As such a barrier, it ought to be capable of resisting the penetration of flames for 15 minutes. Theoretically at least, that would give you enough time to get the airplane on the ground safely.

Stainless steel firewall shields, installed around wires, cables, engine controls and through rubber grommets/asbestos washers, will provide the ultimate protection against flame penetration of the firewall.

SOURCES FOR FIREWALL GROMMET-SHIELDS

First, for the record, I do not know first hand of a reliable, readily available commercial source for those firewall shields — unless, that is, you are willing to make your own.

Both Piper and Cessna aircraft have long used firewall grommet shields (or plates as Piper refers to them). Perhaps more Pipers have more of them installed per aircraft than do any of the other certificated aircraft.

That being the case, you would assume that a well stocked Piper (or Cessna) parts department should have them, or at least be able to obtain whatever you need. Apparently this is not so. At least not in this neck of the woods . . . and I think I understand why.

When an aircraft leaves the plant, it is complete and resplendent down to its very new protective firewall shields screwed to the firewall. During the life of the aircraft there is absolutely no need to remove these protective shields. This means it is most unlikely that any Cessna or Piper owner would ever need such a part. So, why should any parts department stock them? Nevertheless, you would think they could, at least, find one or two part numbers in their catalogs for the things and order them for you.

If you want to check out your local Piper or Cessna parts departments for these shields, here are some typical part numbers you can ask for.

Cessna — Various aircraft models have these firewall grommet shields installed.

(a) S-352 is a common single place shield.

(b) S1095-1 is a two-piece split shield (order two pieces per installation). The dash numbers run from -1 through -6 for the most frequently installed sizes. A S1095-4, for example, accommodates 1/2" diameter wire bundles. The larger the dash number the larger hole is in the shield and the larger the wire bundle it can accommodate.

Piper — Try this part number, PN 18321-00. As mentioned above, I think Piper calls their firewall shields "plates".

Anyway, these are the best I could come up with from my very limited reference library.

My own preferred source for these firewall shields (when I can find some) is, you guessed it — the Fly Markets at Oshkosh, Sun 'n Fun or Kerrville, TX.

There is yet another source. I have frequently relied on this as a more positive source — some locally wrecked aircraft, or an aircraft salvage yard.

Aircraft salvage yard operators are usually quite accommodating and will allow you to remove what you need from one of their "junked" aircraft's stripped firewalls . . . and at a reasonable price, too. Actually, if you are buying other parts, they may not even charge you the two or three shields you need.

These firewall shields are attached to the metal firewall with two cross point sheet metal screws. Ordinar-

ENGINE BAFFLES 4

Making Better Baffles

BAFFLES . . . you must have them for your engine installation, even if you have to make them yourself, unless, of course, you are going to give some liquid-cooled auto engine conversion a try, instead.

Otherwise, any of the air-cooled engines like the Continentals, Lycomings and, yes, VW conversions, too, must have properly designed and tightly fitted baffles in order to obtain and maintain normal engine operating temperatures.

BAFFLE INFORMATION SOURCES

Before you start cutting metal for a set of engine baffles, it might be a good idea to review and enhance your baffling knowledge. Here's how:

1. Examine a few other aircraft at a local airport where there is some on-going maintenance activity (cowlings removed, etc.). There you should be able to look at a few baffle installations and see how they are made and installed.

Not all of the baffle installations you look at will be good examples, but viewing a few different types should give you better ideas of how to go about making your own set.

2. Review and study all the baffling information you can find . . . it won't be much. Just about the only source (outside of number one cited above) is the EAA. The most detailed information EAA has on the subject will probably be that contained in my book, "FIREWALL FORWARD".

If you are building one of the kits like the RV-4, RV-6, Glasair, etc., the plans may already contain the recommended baffle patterns. In some instances, unfinished baffle kits are also available.

At the point, when your project is nearing completion, you may not consider the making of a set of engine baffles as one of the more pleasurable tasks you, as a homebuilder, have yet to complete. Nevertheless, it is an interesting one, and an important one.

Actually, for my part, I have always found the fabrication of a good set of baffles to be a rather satisfying experience.

I must confess, though, that I have had my share of making poorly fitting baffle parts over again.

Since the typical baffle is simple and rather inexpensive to remake, there is nothing much to worry about. Just start cutting your baffle parts out and it will all come together for you.

BAFFLES IN GENERAL

Baffles, since they are fabricated from thin aluminum sheet, are very easy to cut out, bend and assemble . . . assuming, of course, you have good patterns or templates and you understand how to install the baffles so that they will do what they are supposed to do.

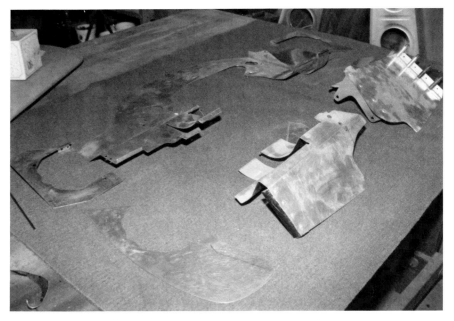

This is what the individual baffles look like before installation. Approximately 11 separate baffles, plus several small brackets, are required for a typical 4 cylinder Lycoming.

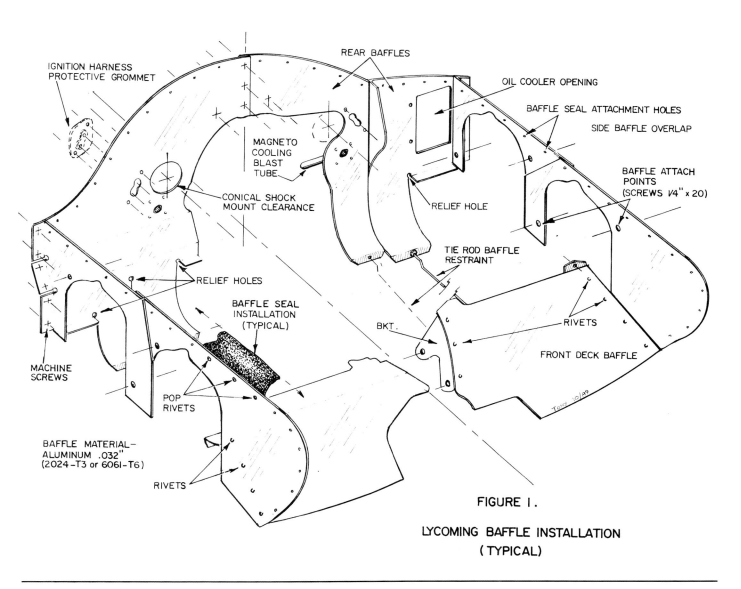

IGNITION HARNESS PROTECTIVE GROMMET

REAR BAFFLES

OIL COOLER OPENING

BAFFLE SEAL ATTACHMENT HOLES

SIDE BAFFLE OVERLAP

MAGNETO COOLING BLAST TUBE

BAFFLE ATTACH POINTS (SCREWS 1/4" x 20)

CONICAL SHOCK MOUNT CLEARANCE

RELIEF HOLE

RELIEF HOLES

TIE ROD BAFFLE RESTRAINT

BAFFLE SEAL INSTALLATION (TYPICAL)

BKT.

RIVETS

FRONT DECK BAFFLE

MACHINE SCREWS

POP RIVETS

BAFFLE MATERIAL— ALUMINUM .032" (2024-T3 or 6061-T6)

RIVETS

FIGURE 1.

LYCOMING BAFFLE INSTALLATION (TYPICAL)

A Necessary Item for Your Engine Installation

The side baffles are made and installed first because they serve as essential anchor points for the attachment of the rear and front baffles.

This is a bottom view of the front RHS baffles. Notice how the bracket is made to support and brace the inboard end of the front baffle. Look again . . . don't let the reflections on the aluminum confuse you.

Baffles, as you may have surmised, must be formed to fit closely against the cylinder fins, and against the engine crankcase. In addition, it is essential that each baffle segment, or assembly, be firmly secured to the engine and/or to each other to immobilize it.

The rear baffle segments, especially, must be carefully trimmed along the bottom edges so they fit snugly against the engine crankcase. That is, there must be

no sizable gaps between these baffle segments and that hard-to-fit area of the engine crankcase.

Your corner flanges, too, must be accurately bent (on the bend lines) and the corners closely fitted so that none of the cooling air can escape without passing through the engine cooling fins.

MATERIAL NEEDS

Use either .025" or .032" thick aluminum for your baffle material. I would not use anything thicker as it will make your installation needlessly heavier.

You could make the corner baffle of heavier .040" aluminum, if an oil cooler is to be mounted there. However, a small reinforcement angle would serve as well.

The softer 5052 H34 or 6061 T6 aluminum is easier to bend and is not as prone to crack as the 2024 T3 . . . especially in corners.

Let's assume that you are baffling a typical 4 cylinder Lycoming engine. For that job you will need a fairly large piece of aluminum (approximately 36" x 48").

Naturally, the aluminum does not have to be in a single piece. You can just as well use several smaller pieces because there are approximately eleven (11) fairly small individual baffle segments that you will have to cut out.

In any case, you will need the approximate equivalent of, roughly, 12 sq. ft. of aluminum. This should provide enough material to allow you to make at least one piece over again . . . if you goof, or don't like the fit of your initial attempt.

TEMPLATE AND PATTERN LAYOUT

I would suggest you place all of your templates, or paper patterns, on the metal, and then switch them around until you have an arrangement that requires the minimum of material. Be careful. Don't try to be

ROTARY FILE

BAFFLE

DRILL PRESS

ROTARY FILE

BAFFLE BEING SHAPED

WOOD BLOCK SUPPORT

DRILL PRESS TABLE

TONY 10-89

FIGURE 2.
SHAPING BAFFLE CUT-OUTS

Baffling for Your Lycoming

My earlier book, "Firewall Forward," contains a chapter entitled, "Baffling Business". It gives, in detail, the information and the template layout patterns necessary for making a set of engine baffles for the small C-85 and O-200 Continental engines.

So, it seems only fair (and about time) I accorded the popular 4 cylinder Lycoming engines the same, if somewhat belated, attention.

Actually, broadly speaking, there is very little difference in the way 4-cylinder Continental and Lycoming engines are baffled. The Lycomings, because of their large starter ring gear, require a slightly different baffling up front. Then, too, while the Continental side baffles are usually made in one piece, the Lycoming practice is to make two separate baffles for each side. There are other subtle differences — like points of attachment (Lycoming has more of them), and the design of the inter-cylinder baffles.

I will confine my baffling exposé to conventional tractor installations. By that I mean those installations that have the propeller up front where you can see it if it stops.

As you know, in a conventional 4-cylinder air cooled engine installation, the cooling air is allowed to enter the cowling just behind the propeller through inlets, and into the chamber-like space above the engine. However, we know there is more to this business of cooling an aircooled engine than merely causing air to flow into the engine compartment and past the engine.

The amount of cooling the engine would get from such a haphazard flow of cooling air would be inadequate as the incoming air would be spewed all over the engine compartment, and only a small portion of it would make its way down through the cylinders' cooling fins. For this reason, it is necessary to install barriers (baffles) inside the engine compartment, so designed as to force the cooling air down through the cylinder fins. In effect, this baffling limits the amount of air entering the engine compartment to that which will effectively cool the engine. That, in turn, reduces cooling drag and the wasteful use of engine power for ineffective cooling.

Your basic objective in baffling the engine, therefore, is to provide a pressurized "leak-proof" chamber in which the cooling air has no alternative but to exit down through the hot cylinder fins, picking up engine heat as it scoots on out thorugh the air outlets provided. In doing so, the engine will benefit from the maximum potential cooling for a given atmospheric temperature and airspeed. Although this is a very simplified, very broad generalization of the concept, I think it conveys the basic idea of what this baffling effort is all about.

THE NEW ENGINE

Take a good overall look at that engine of yours. A new engine, or one that has been freshly overhauled by an engine shop, will be as naked as a new born babe. It will, undoubtedly, be a basic engine unit (I hate to use the term "stripped") uncluttered by the non-presence of a lot of the goodies you will need. It most probably will not have any baffles or attachment brackets — with one exception. Your engine should already have the inner-cylinder baffles installed. These are specially designed and fabricated baffles which are installed at the Lycoming factory before the engine leaves the premises. These baffles (between the cylinders) always stay with the engine. However, to be sure you have yours, check your engine to see if they are installed, and are in a serviceable condition. Your engine must have these baffles installed or it won't cool properly no matter how effective your other baffling might be.

THE USED ENGINE

A used engine can be just as skimpily equipped and as barren as a new engine. On the other hand, you might be fortunate in having an engine that is already equipped with baffles. Chances are though that they may not be in very good condition. Some of the baffles may fit poorly and you may even find a crack here and there. Also, there is the likelihood that the installed baffles are too short in some places and too tall in others. Still, a set of baffles — good or bad — can be a valuable resource for you.

A serviceable set of baffles that happens to be too tall can always be trimmed down with a pair of aviation tin snips. On the other hand, baffles too short for your cowling may have to be replaced. If you don't want to go to all that work, you could modify them by riveting extension pieces to bridge the gap. It won't look as nice as a single piece baffle but most likely nobody will notice it or comment on it.

At any rate, don't throw away that old set of baffles even if they are not airworthy. At the very least, you could clean and disassemble them and use them for patterns.

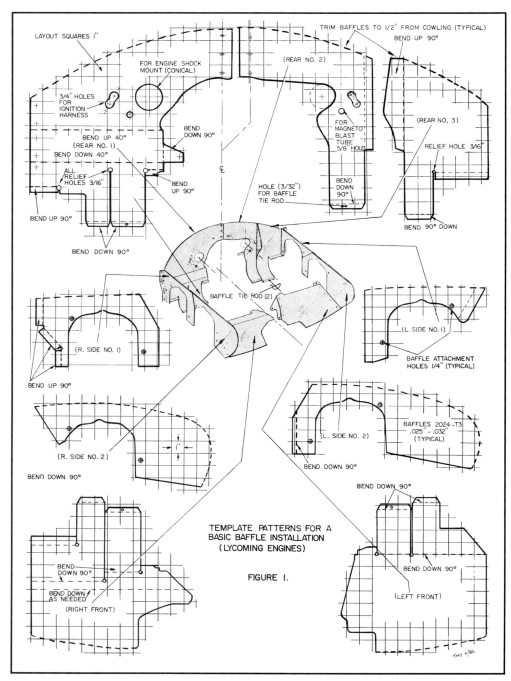

LAYOUT SQUARES 1"

FOR ENGINE SHOCK MOUNT (CONICAL)

TRIM BAFFLES TO 1/2" FROM COWLING (TYPICAL)
BEND UP 90°

(REAR NO. 2)

3/4" HOLES FOR IGNITION HARNESS

FOR MAGNETO BLAST TUBE 5/8" HOLE

(REAR NO. 3)

BEND DOWN 90°

BEND UP 40° (REAR NO. I)
BEND DOWN 40°

RELIEF HOLE 3/16"

ALL RELIEF HOLES 3/16"

BEND UP 90°

HOLE (3/32") FOR BAFFLE TIE ROD

BEND DOWN 90°

BEND UP 90°

BEND 90° DOWN

BEND DOWN 90°

BAFFLE TIE ROD (2)

(R. SIDE NO. I)

(L. SIDE NO. I)

BAFFLE ATTACHMENT HOLES 1/4" (TYPICAL)

BEND UP 90°

(R. SIDE NO. 2)

1"

(L. SIDE NO. 2)

BAFFLES 2024-T3 .025"-.032" (TYPICAL)

BEND DOWN 90°

BEND DOWN 90°

BEND DOWN 90°

BEND DOWN 90°

TEMPLATE PATTERNS FOR A BASIC BAFFLE INSTALLATION (LYCOMING ENGINES)

FIGURE I.

BEND DOWN 90°

BEND DOWN AS NEEDED

(RIGHT FRONT)

BEND DOWN 90°

(LEFT FRONT)

Tony 6/86

Try to arrange your templates without wasting a lot of aluminum . . . you may have to make a piece over again. Remember, you will have to be able to cut out each piece, so allow space for cutting tool maneuvering.

70

When you do make your new set of baffles, don't forget to allow extra material along the top edges where it may be needed. While you are at it, take the opportunity to improve the fit of each individual baffle. Just because the baffles were factory made is no assurance that they were originally fitted to as close a tolerance as many an enlightened homebuilder sets for himself.

ON BUYING A SET OF BAFFLES

Some kit producers and independent entrepreneurs provide baffle kits for a particular engine and, perhaps, a specific aircraft design. Of those that I have seen, a number of them are rather crude and relatively unfinished. They appear to have been roughly cut and have edges and corners that have not been deburred. You probably would be better off to make your own rather than order such a set. Other baffles I have seen are well finished pieces exhibiting good workmanship — and quite complete — with predrilled or marked attachment holes. Baffles like that would probably be worth the extra price charged. In other words, I would

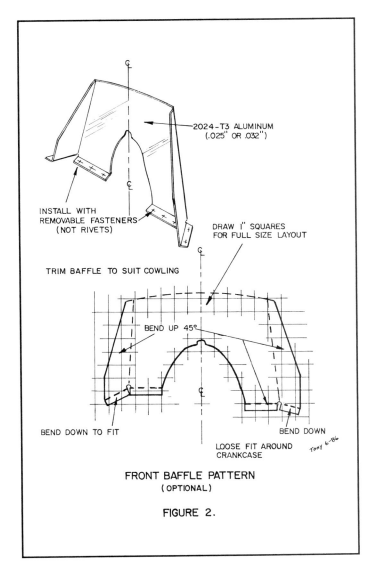

2024-T3 ALUMINUM (.025" OR .032")

INSTALL WITH REMOVABLE FASTENERS (NOT RIVETS)

TRIM BAFFLE TO SUIT COWLING

DRAW I" SQUARES FOR FULL SIZE LAYOUT

BEND UP 45°

BEND DOWN TO FIT

BEND DOWN

LOOSE FIT AROUND CRANKCASE

Tony 6-86

FRONT BAFFLE PATTERN
(OPTIONAL)

FIGURE 2.

infer that it might be a good idea to check with other builders to find out just what you would be getting. Avoid buying a pig in a poke (you wouldn't want it on board anyway, would you?).

THOUGHTS ABOUT BAFFLE DESIGN

There is very little variation in the design of the engine baffles you see installed in the general "Wichita Fleet". The differences, for the most part, seem to be up front where the cooling air enters the cowling. Some installations employ a level or a gradually sloped, ramp-like, baffle which causes the air to flow smoothly up to the cylinders and thence into the chamber above the engine. Further down the flight line you are sure to see an installation where the front of the engine is blocked by a perpendicular wall of baffles which appear to be capable of stopping the cooling air in its tracks. To me, it would seem that such an installation would be more appropriate for a bull dozer rather than a fast airplane. Still, these manufacturers are an enterprising lot and I am sure they have their reasons for that sort of turbulent entry for the cooling air.

Lycoming engines have a peculiar design feature — a huge starter ring gear impaled on the crankshaft smack-dab behind the propeller. It effectively interferes with streamlining efforts and complicates cowling design because it gets in the way of the cooling air. However, thanks to large spinners and prop extensions, this blunting effect can be greatly minimized. It does, nevertheless, introduce a baffling challenge in that it is very difficult to seal the area behind the starter ring gear and the crankcase sufficiently enough that the cooling air doesn't take a shortcut and bypass the cylinder fins.

ACCURATE BAFFLE TEMPLATES

It is difficult to make a complete set of baffles without the benefit of full sized patterns or templates. Unless you do have access to a set of templates, I'm afraid you will have to make your own.

Baffle templates are important if you want to save time and avoid wasting expensive aluminum. Without the use of templates, you may find, to your disgust, that you have to remake several baffles before you obtain an acceptable fit. The most aggravating difficulty will stem from your efforts to locate the baffle attachment holes. If you guess wrong, you will have a baffle with a badly elongated hole or two. Elongated holes are an embarrassment to the viewer and to the owner alike. In a baffle it is not a critical structural matter usually . . . just embarrassing.

You can make a full sized set of templates by starting with the baffle patterns illustrated in Figure 1. Simply draw a bunch of one inch squares across a manila folder and trace the lines as shown, from one square to another. All of the baffles can be laid out in this manner quite quickly.

Use manila folders as your template material un-

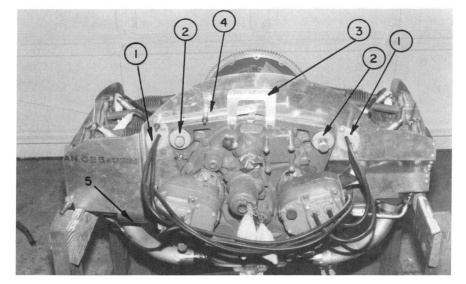

Baffling details on this Lycoming 0-320 include: ignition harness grommets (1), conical shock mounts (2), rear baffle center attach bracket (3), aluminum stiffener (4), left rear baffle showing curvature around the bottom of the cylinder barrel (5).

This front view shows the ignition harness openings (1), conical shock mount openings (2), rear bulkhead brace fasteners (3), and the front inlet entry baffles (4) and (5). Note that they cover the bottom half of the cylinder barrels only.

There is more than one way to baffle an engine. Here's another variation. In essence, you want all the air entering the cowling to be forced down through the cylinder cooling fins . . . well, there are some concessions, aren't there?

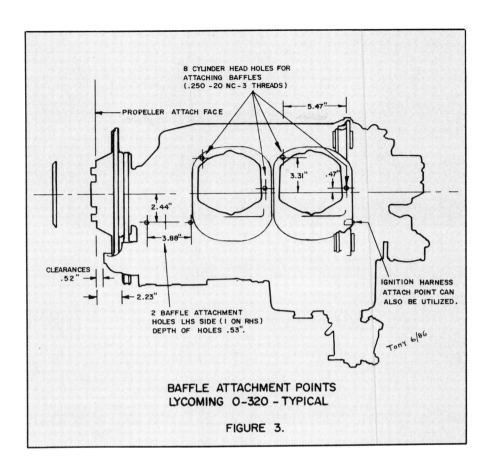

8 CYLINDER HEAD HOLES FOR
ATTACHING BAFFLES
(.250 -20 NC - 3 THREADS)

PROPELLER ATTACH FACE

5.47"

3.31"   .47"

2.44"

3.88"

CLEARANCES
.52"

2.23"

2 BAFFLE ATTACHMENT
HOLES LHS SIDE (I ON RHS)
DEPTH OF HOLES .53".

IGNITION HARNESS
ATTACH POINT CAN
ALSO BE UTILIZED.

Tony 6/86

**BAFFLE ATTACHMENT POINTS
LYCOMING O-320 - TYPICAL**

FIGURE 3.

less you intend for them to be used many times over. In that case, a set of aluminum templates would be better. the light cardboard quality of a manila folder makes it easy to cut with scissors.

After cutting out a rough pattern, place it on the engine to check its fit. Snip away any tight areas with scissors until the template fits perfectly. If parts of the template have been cut in too deeply, don't worry, the fix is easy. Just bridge those gaps with small pieces of masking tape. continue this cut and patch process until you are satisifed with the fit.

Next, tape that corrected template to the engine with pieces of masking tape in preparation for locating the baffle attachment holes. How would you do it? You can't see through a manila folder, can you? I have tried probing around for the underlying hole with an ice pick or a metal center punch with some success. After locating the right spot, I would poke the ice pick through the template and into the hole. This really marks the hole's location all right. But, somehow, I have never been able to drill all the baffle holes accurately from this template. One problem, I suppose, is due to the ragged edges around the punched hole which makes it difficult to transfer the exact center of the hole with a punch to the metal baffle. As a result, after the holes are drilled, one or two may be off enough that they must be elongated slightly before the fasteners will go in.

Here is a more accurate way to locate your baffle attachment holes. Round the end of a short piece of dowel and use it to rub over the cardboard template in the area where the hole is known to be. You will feel the thin cardboard give way slightly when you pass over the underlying hole. Stop right there and twirl the dowel between your fingers over that hole location. As you do, the sharp edges of the screw hole will cause an embossed image of the hole to appear on the template as a beautiful round circle.

It would be easy to locate the baffle mounting holes if you could see where they were, right? Well, why not use a clear plastic sheet for the template? It would have to be fairly thin and stiff . . . maybe .010" thick.

MAKING THE BAFFLES

After checking the fit of your template on the engine, remove it and trace it onto your aluminum baffle material.

Most builders use either .025" or .032" thick aluminum for their baffles.

2024T3 aluminum is commonly used but some builders prefer to use the softer 6061T4 or 6061T6 because it is more readily available and less expensive than 2024T3 aluminum.

Another good grade to use is the 5052 H32, or H34, series. It has excellent workability and a fatigue

What homebuilder would baffle his engine using this "Great Wall" concept?

A front baffle is being fitted in this installation. Note the flat entry treatment for the inlet baffle.

The right rear corner of this 0-320 shows how tightly the baffling fits. Removable fasteners are used so that baffling may be removed. Use rivets only where parts will not need to be separated for removal.

This view shows the entry baffle (A) which is made in one piece. Note how the bottom portions curve tightly around the cylinder barrel.

strength higher than most other aluminum alloys.

The softer grades of aluminum are more popular with homebuilders because they feel the softer material is less prone to crack.

Tape the baffle template to the aluminum blank with a few scraps of masking tape to insure that the template will not slide while you are tracing it. Trace the template's outline onto the aluminum with an indelible ink marking pen. (A SHARPIE pen is perfect — most stationery counters have them.) After the tracing is completed, carefully make your center punchmarks through the template every place you have an embossed hole location. Drill the baffle attachment holes with a 1/4" bit.

The easiest way to cut out baffles is on a bandsaw fitted with a 1/4" metal cutting blade. You can cut aluminum with the blade running at regular speed.

Baffles can also be cut out with aviation tin snips. The thin metal will be easy to cut but the process will take longer. This is because tin snips leave little crimp marks along the line of cut. These must be removed by filing as they might become starting places for cracks. Leave a good 1/16" extra margin when using tin snips.

All edges should be deburred or filed smooth with smooth cut files. You will probably use a flat file, a half

round file and a small round file in finishing the baffles. If a lot of material must be trimmed away, a rotary file chucked in a drill press can do the job quickly — but be careful.

I would suggest you temporarily install each baffle as you complete it to simplify the fitting of the adjacent baffle.

When making some baffles you may find it necessary to cut a few long slits to separate the portions of the baffle that must be bent to curve around the bottoms of the cylinders. These slits, or cuts, can be made with a hacksaw fitted with a fine tooth blade. Cut the metal baffle with the blade tilted to a shallow angle in order to obtain the straightest cut.

RELIEF HOLES

When a portion of a baffle must be bent to form a corner or a similarly difficult bend, it is necessary to drill a relief hole at the junction of such bends. Use a 3/16" drill. Chamfer each drilled relief hole with a larger diameter drill bit held between your fingers and twirled lightly over the hole to remove the sharp edges and chips. Do this faithfully for each hole you drill in the baffles.

RADIUS OF BEND REMINDER

Any bends to be made in the baffles should have a rather large radius to avoid overstressing the stiff, somewhat brittle 2024 T3 aluminum. Those using the softer 6061 T6 can make their bends somewhat sharper. This is really no great problem when working with thin material (.025" or .032"). However, the bend radius should be no less than 3 times the thickness of the baffle material. That would be, say .075" radius. This is about the same radius you would get if you were to bend the metal baffle around a 5/32" drill bit or a rod for a 90 degree bend.

CLOSE FIT ESSENTIAL

The final and permanent installation of the various baffle sections can best be done with the engine installed in the aircraft — before you begin to install and hook up any of the wiring or plumbing. This will afford you the advantage of having good access to all parts of the engine while you work on the baffles.

If it is more convenient you could, almost as well, fit your metal baffles to the uninstalled engine while it is still in your workshop.

Now would be a good time to make those small final adjustments to the fit of each individual baffle.

Does each baffle fit snugly agaisnt the crankcase and against its adjacent baffle? Be prepared to remake any piece that doesn't fit closely. By closely, I mean like a zero tolerance against the crankcase . . . well, maybe a 1/16 inch gap can be accepted for the moment. You should realize, though, that allowing a 1/8 inch gap here and another there can soon add up to several square inches of air leaks.

It is essential that every bit of the air entering the engine compartment be used effectively for cooling and not be allowed to escape without doing its part. Any air

Fitting of the baffles may be done before the engine is installed. In that event, it could be suspended from a hoist or supported in a mobile stand as shown here.

that blows past the baffles without being forced down through the cylinder fins equates to so much wasted engine power. Not only that, you may find yourself with a serious engine cooling problem on your first flight. Well, so much for the halftime pep talk.

BAFFLE ASSEMBLY AND INSTALLATION TIPS

You may one day have to remove your baffles, or at least some portion of them, for maintenance or repair . . . maybe even replacement. To be prepared for such an eventuality it would be wise to assemble certain baffles as subassemblies. By this I mean permenently rivet together only those baffle sections which can be installed and removed as a unit from the engine. All

Here is an interesting baffling job. In some installations it may be necessary to baffle and seal the lower area behind the starter ring gear. This is one way to do it. Ever think of hanging a landing light off your engine baffles?

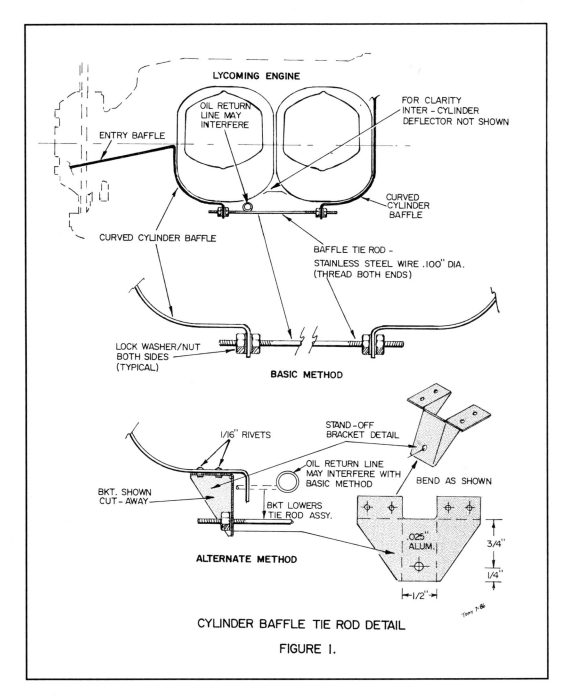

LYCOMING ENGINE

ENTRY BAFFLE

OIL RETURN LINE MAY INTERFERE

FOR CLARITY INTER - CYLINDER DEFLECTOR NOT SHOWN

CURVED CYLINDER BAFFLE

CURVED CYLINDER BAFFLE

BAFFLE TIE ROD - STAINLESS STEEL WIRE .100" DIA. (THREAD BOTH ENDS)

LOCK WASHER/NUT BOTH SIDES (TYPICAL)

BASIC METHOD

1/16" RIVETS

STAND -OFF BRACKET DETAIL

OIL RETURN LINE MAY INTERFERE WITH BASIC METHOD

BEND AS SHOWN

BKT. SHOWN CUT - AWAY

BKT LOWERS TIE ROD ASSY.

.025" ALUM.

3/4"

1/4"

1/2"

Tony 7-86

ALTERNATE METHOD

CYLINDER BAFFLE TIE ROD DETAIL

FIGURE I.

other baffles will have to be joined with removable fasteners. Wherever a wrench or screw driver access from one side is difficult, consider installing plate nuts (anchor nuts).

Lycoming engines have a generous number of holes tapped into the engine at strategic locations strictly for the purpose of attaching baffles. These baffle attachment holes are approximately 1/2 inch deep and are tapped to accept .250-20NC-3 x 1/2 inch cap screw fasteners. Even so, it might take a bit of ingenuity to design the type of bracket you need to take advantage of the nearest baffle attachment hole(s).

Strive for a rigid installation. The more rigid your baffle installation, the less likely that you will ever experience baffle cracking problems due to vibration induced fatigue in the thin metal.

Along this line, Lycoming has a good method for immobilizing the curved baffle ends that curve around the bottom of the cylinders. These curved baffle ends are joined together by a baffle tie rod which holds the baffle snugly against the cylinder fins (see Figure 1). You may find it necessary to make and rivet small stand-off brackets to the baffle ends as shown to be assured that the baffle tie rod clears the oil return line from the rocker box.

If you prefer, you could use .040" stainless steel twisted safety wire instead of the tie rods, illustrated in Figure 1, to tie the two curved baffle ends together.

This builder allowed his baffle seal strips to bend backwards. This is wrong. Air pressure build-up will force the strips away from the cowling leaving a gap for the air to escape. If he doesn't have a cooling problem it is because the metal baffles were fitted very close against the cowling and the seals are at least partially effective.

Slip a length of 1/4" Nylaflow plastic tubing over the twisted wires to eliminate the risk of chafing against the oil return line.

HOLES AND OPENINGS?

First, I do my best to convince you that the baffles should be tight fitting and provide a leakproof pressure chamber over the engine and now I am about to concede that it is O.K. to put some holes in the baffles deliberately. As you know, ideals and realities are often in conflict, and so it is with our basic baffling concept. Some holes in baffles are justifiable because they are needed to meet installation requirements or are essential to the safe operation of the engine. Here are a few:

1. The two openings through which the ignition wires must pass. These openings must be large enough to allow the connector fittings to pass through. The holes are usually sealed with standard plastic diamond shaped grommets screwed to the baffle.

2. The two holes for the magneto cooling blast tubes. Without this cooling air for the magnetos they could suffer failure due to extremely high magneto temperatures. Bendix magnetos, for example, cannot tolerate temperatures much over 350 degrees F before suffering deterioration and possible failure (see Figure 2).

3. The two large holes for the engine shock mounts. These holes, fortunately, are almost completely taken up by the shock mount assemblies.

4. The large opening for the oil cooler, when located in a back or front baffle.

5. The hole for the cooling air blast tube to the generator or alternator.

The wide seal strips and method of installing them insures a good air seal against the cowling.

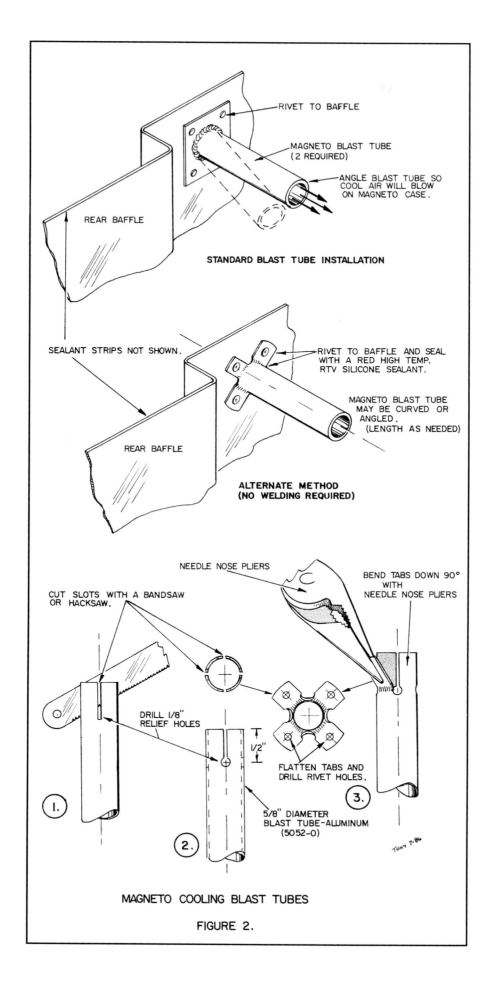

RIVET TO BAFFLE

MAGNETO BLAST TUBE
(2 REQUIRED)

ANGLE BLAST TUBE SO
COOL AIR WILL BLOW
ON MAGNETO CASE.

REAR BAFFLE

STANDARD BLAST TUBE INSTALLATION

SEALANT STRIPS NOT SHOWN.

RIVET TO BAFFLE AND SEAL
WITH A RED HIGH TEMP.
RTV SILICONE SEALANT.

MAGNETO BLAST TUBE
MAY BE CURVED OR
ANGLED.
(LENGTH AS NEEDED)

REAR BAFFLE

**ALTERNATE METHOD
(NO WELDING REQUIRED)**

NEEDLE NOSE PLIERS

BEND TABS DOWN 90°
WITH
NEEDLE NOSE PLIERS

CUT SLOTS WITH A BANDSAW
OR HACKSAW.

DRILL 1/8"
RELIEF HOLES

1/2"

FLATTEN TABS AND
DRILL RIVET HOLES.

1.

2.

3.

5/8" DIAMETER
BLAST TUBE-ALUMINUM
(5052-0)

Tony 7-86

MAGNETO COOLING BLAST TUBES

FIGURE 2.

The early stage of fitting the baffles. This builder started with the side baffles and is now fitting the back baffle pieces. If the piece fits good — keep it. If not, make it over.

6. The large 3 inch to 3-1/2 inch opening in the rear baffle for ducting air to the carburetor or fuel injector (sometimes).

7. The hole for the ducting of cooling air to a shrouded engine fuel pump (optional).

8. An opening for ducting cooling air to the cabin (optional).

That is a surprising number of holes, isn't it? Some baffle installations have them all. Fortunately, a number of them are not essential and your installation could probably do without them by making alternative provisions. Anyway, you should seriously question the need for some of them before punching your baffles full of holes.

OIL COOLER LOCATION AND INSTALLATION

You really have but three good options for locating the oil cooler. Mount it up front in the front entry baffle on the left side (just ahead of the number 2 cylinder), locate it in the back baffle (either side) or mount it remoted to some part of the firewall.

The simplest and lightest installations are those with the oil cooler mounted in the left side rear baffle. this is because the connecting lines to the accessory section are the shortest and most direct from this kind of installation. Another advantage this location offers is that the oil cooler is easier to mount securely. Incidentally, if you use this location, modify your aft left side baffle so that it will space the oil cooler back about one inch (or slightly more) from the number 4 cylinder fins.

Mounting the oil cooler in the front left baffle has the disadvantage of being more difficult to position effectively. I've seen some installation where the oil cooler was partially blocking the inlet air. In addition, it also dumped the hot air from the oil cooler into the upper engine compartment . . . but I don't imagine that you would do anything like that. Of course, the up-front location will require the installation of much longer oil

This is the correct way to orient the baffle seals. Force them to curve inward toward the center of the engine. Air pressure will then hold the seals tight against the cowling. Lap seal strips at point "A" so that the baffles can be removed if need be.

A popular location for the oil cooler is off the back baffle, either on the right side or left side. In some cases your engine mount may not allow sufficient clearance. This is an efficient location as the connecting hoses can be relatively short.

An up front oil cooler is generally located on the left side as there is more space. Your oil lines have to be quite long as you can see.

An up front oil cooler can be flush mounted as in this installation. Remember, mounting the oil cooler up front will require longer hoses. Note that the area behind the starter ring gear is baffled and sealed.

An enclosed pressure chamber baffle installation is very efficient and virtually eliminates the need for those floppy baffle seal strips. Access to the top spark plugs is difficult and the pressure chamber must be made easy to disassemble. Use screws and nut plates or piano hinge wire connectors.

The same pressure chamber cooling installation as viewed from the left side of the engine. Note the rounded aft end of the enclosure. This type of installation requires more space above the engine than does a conventional baffle/seal unit.

Here is another version of the enclosed pressure chamber cooling idea. This installation is on a BD-4 and has proven to be very effective. It is simple to make and is just about leak proof. Views from all sides reveal exactly how the chamber is constructed. Note the generous use of screws to facilitate access and removal.

A three quarter view of the pressure chamber as seen from the right hand side. A minimum amount of sealant strips is still required at the air inlet areas.

If yours is a stock kit cowling, the inlet and outlet areas provided should be just about right for your engine installation. However, be sure your exhaust pipes, braces and other parts don't reduce the total effective area of the air outlets. The air outlet areas should be somewhat larger than the total inlet areas.

blocked or severely restricted. This will certainly inhibit the proper cooling of the oil and the engine.

The three most popular locations for the oil cooler are:

1. Up front somewhere in the front baffle deck.

2. On the left aft baffle. Occasionally you will find the cooler installed on the right rear baffle but the oil lines will have to be longer.

3. Remotely mounted, usually on the firewall.

The simplest and lightest installation is the one with the oil cooler mounted in the left rear baffle. A mistaken belief prevails that the cooling air reaching the oil cooler in this location will have been heated somewhat in passing over the cylinders. This is not so . . . not when there is a balanced flow of air through the cowling inlets and outlets.

COWL FLAPS?

The cooling benefits realized from the installation of cowl flaps are the greatest for high performance aircraft. Without cowl flaps the engine temperatures run very high during climbs to altitude and tend to run very cool in cruise.

Cowl flaps provide a cockpit controllable low-drag variable cooling air outlet. They can minimize the high percentage of cooling air drag otherwise present in a clean fast airplane.

Cowl flaps result in a heavier, more complex installation. It also becomes necessary in most installations to disconnect the cowl flaps before removing the cowling. In spite of these minor annoyances, cowl flaps can be essential in controlling engine temperatures . . . especially on the ground, and during climbs to altitude. Furthermore, cooling drag at cruise can be reduced.

A newly overhauled engine will often run hotter the first few hours. If this situation is applicable, take this into consideration. If your oil temperatures does not actually reach the redline in flight, you should be able to closely monitor the engine oil temperature's behavior for a few flights before undertaking more drastic measures.

Here is something else you should know about aircraft temperature gauges in general. Some are temperature compensated, some are not. What difference does that make? It could be quite significant. In fact, your engine may be running hotter (or cooler) than the temperature gauge indicates. Check that out, too.

"I'd rather be flying."

Carl Schuppel

All metal RV-4 with a 200 hp Lycoming IO-360 A1B6 engine installed.

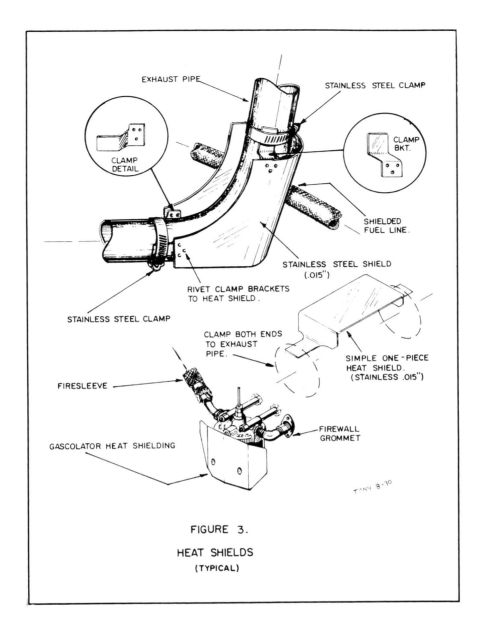

EXHAUST PIPE

STAINLESS STEEL CLAMP

CLAMP DETAIL

CLAMP BKT.

SHIELDED FUEL LINE.

STAINLESS STEEL SHIELD (.015")

RIVET CLAMP BRACKETS TO HEAT SHIELD.

STAINLESS STEEL CLAMP

CLAMP BOTH ENDS TO EXHAUST PIPE.

SIMPLE ONE-PIECE HEAT SHIELD. (STAINLESS .015")

FIRESLEEVE

GASCOLATOR HEAT SHIELDING

FIREWALL GROMMET

FIGURE 3.

HEAT SHIELDS

(TYPICAL)

This is a firewall mounted gadget that looks something like a small high technology coffee percolator.

Some Piper aircraft utilize these separators for their Lycoming installations. Maybe you can find one in an aircraft salvage yard or at some fly-in "Fly Market" or "Country Store". However, an enterprising builder could make his own.

Both Aircraft Spruce & Specialty Co. and Wicks Aircraft Supply carry a separator with 5/8" outlets which was originally intended for use with Continental engine equipped VariEzes and Long-EZs.

In a typical installation, the oil draining from the separator is returned to the engine crankcase oil supply and the separated oil-free engine breather air is dumped overboard.

I have always used the engine oil filler neck as a return point for the oil draining from the breather separator. This required tapping a hole (1/8" pipe) into the lower end of the oil filler neck. I then connected a 1/4" oil return line from the oil breather/separator to a suitable fitting at the filler neck.

If you want to do the same thing, you should first mark the spot you want the fitting hole to be located before unscrewing the filler neck from the engine. This will ensure that your hole, when drilled and tapped, will be in a location where it will be accessible after reinstalling the filler neck.

Also, don't forget to resafety the filler neck after reinstalling it.

Incidentally, some builders don't like the idea of returning engine breather oil to the engine as condensed water vapor may be present, contaminating the reclaimed oil residue.

When the flights are long enough, however, the oil gets hot enough to vaporize the water and most of the acids, eliminating them from the oil.

On the other hand, if most of your flights are short, it might be better to install a small container near the

Shown here is a heat shield to protect the cowling from being scorched by the hot exhaust pipes that run parallel (and very close) to the cowling. The stainless steel heat shield is clamped to the exhaust pipe with stainless steel clamps.

bottom of the firewall to catch the engine breather residue rather than allowing it to exit freely and blow over the belly of the aircraft. The container would have to be drained periodically.

MAGNETO BLAST TUBES

Magnetos also suffer from excessive engine compartment heat.

To be on the safe side, install a short curved 1/2" tube that will direct cooling air over the magneto case from an opening in the rear engine baffle.

ALTERNATOR COOLING AIR

Many alternators, especially those lightweight, inexpensive 25-35 amp. units builders are installing in their homebuilts, come from Toyotas, Datsuns, and similar vehicles where they operate in a different environment.

Installing one in your homebuilt without providing it with adequate cooling can cause the alternator to be short lived. That is, its diodes could be "fried" due to a lack of cooling air through the rear of the unit where the diodes are located.

The remedy is to pipe ram air from a one inch hole in the front baffle to the back case of the alternator through a length of SCAT ducting.

The difficult part is devising a means to position and secure the outlet end of the ducting so that it blows directly at the rear case of the alternator.

There are all kinds of alternators so it would be a good idea to determine whether or not your particular installation requires any special treatment like changing the pulley size, replacing or removing the fan blades, or piping cooling air into the alternator case, somehow.

Check with your local alternator shop . . . I've already told you everything I think I know.

Lycoming R-680 installed in a Fairchild XNQ-1. Note how engine accessories are readily available for checking or maintenance. A nice feature is the hinged upper cowlings which swing upward and are held open with a metal rod.

Engine Compartment Notes

Installing an engine for the first time always raises a number of questions and uncertainties. You have to make numerous decisions to keep the installation simple and make it work properly, and yet have it conform to accepted aircraft practices.

Unlike commercially produced personal aircraft, the ones we build are rather small by comparison.

Consequently, engine compartment space is quite limited. We, therefore, have to jam the entire exhaust system, oil system and a crucial portion of the fuel system inside a close fitting steamlined cowling.

Ordinarily, the cowling fits so closely that the exhaust pipes, unfortunately, act as unwelcome radiant heaters. Furthermore, the stacks often run so close to the cowling that the fiberglass and paint may char.

Along the same line, the close clearance between the engine and the firewall can be equally troublesome. For example, the engine mount may be so short that there is insufficient space behind for removing the oil filter without having to disconnect and pull the engine away from its mount. Obviously, this is not a fun thing to do everytime you have to change the oil filter.

What other alternative is there? Remove the oil filter permanently? Although there must be more small aircraft engine installations without oil filters than with, I certainly wouldn't want to do that.

Here is another firewall clearance problem. When you try to install a controllable propeller, you may likewise discover to your dismay that there is insufficient space between the engine and the firewall for installing the governor control.

Learning of these space restrictions after you have connected the engine to the engine mount can be disheartening.

On the other hand, if you are aware of these problems before hanging the engine, you can, in spite of your disappointment, fairly easily modify the firewall by adding the necessary recessed area to make it possible to remove the oil filter. If necessary, you could make the recess portion large enough to also accommodate the propeller governor installation.

Can you imagine what a monumental job it would be if you had to cut into the firewall and construct a recessed area in it with the engine installed?

Many builders will not know they have a clearance problem until they obtain the engine and take a few measurements. It would be wise, therefore, to check with other builders to see if they had to cope with this difficulty.

Would rerouting this SCAT ventilation duct further away from the engine exhaust flanges lessen the exposure risk from fire in event of a broken exhaust stack?

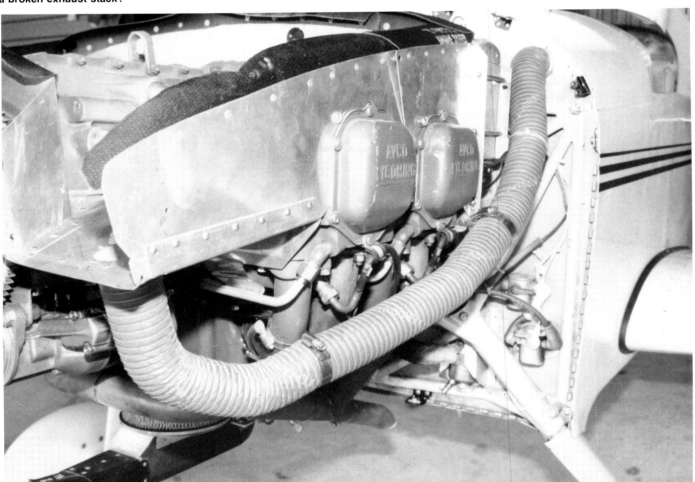

MAKING THE FIREWALL RECESS

The firewall is intended as a fire barrier and is therefore installed as a stainless steel or galvanized sheet approximately .016" thick. These metals are completely fireproof and conform to recommended federal standards for firewalls.

This means that when you cut out a portion of the firewall for the recess, you should be prepared to construct the insert with a like fireproof material.

Aluminum, though easier to work, is not an acceptable material for the recess unless it can be otherwise protected in an acceptable manner. The melting point of aluminum is approximately 1100 to 1200 degrees F. . . . that is a far lower temperature than the recommended 2000 degree F. protection afforded by fireproof materials.

Most builders who have to modify their firewall, construct an open ended box of stainless steel and pop rivet it into the opening. Often, this results in a rather poorly fitting inset that requires additional sealing.

Since I had no intention of using a constant speed prop, all I needed was a small recess area which would permit the removal of the oil filter.

It seemed to me that a stainless steel mixing bowl inserted in and riveted to the firewall would make an ideal recessed area. After all, it is fireproof and has no corners or joints through which flames could penetrate.

The major problem would be in locating a stainless steel bowl with a flanged edge wide enough to rivet to the firewall.

I needed a steel bowl about 7 inches in diameter for my RV-6A firewall. I was surprised to locate one in the household wares aisle of an Albertsons super market (they had different sizes) for a mere $2.79. The only drawback was that it had a small rolled edge. There was no way I could drill rivet holes through it for the firewall installation without modification.

I modified the bowl by carefully grinding away a minimum amount of the rolled edge, all around the

bowl, using a bench grinder. The razor sharp edge remaining was flattened and made less lethal with a file.

Next, I built a hollowed plywood jig to hold the bowl in an upright position so that its edge protruded above the plywood surface by approximately 5/16".

The steel bowl was then clamped in the plywood holder and the edges were slowly worked down with a rubber mallet.

Stainless steel is quite maleable and it is possible to hammer a flattened edge around the steel bowl wide enough to accept 3/32" rivets. The completed installation is attractive, and one you'd be proud to show off as there are no gaps or corners where dirt and oil can accumulate. But even with the extra recessed depth provided by the steel bowl, the job of removing the oil filter won't be any the less messy . . . easier and quicker perhaps, but just as messy.

A FIREWALL AIR DUCT SHUT OFF?

The picture shown on page 99 first appeared in SPORT AVIATION, March 1991 in my article, "Here is a Good Ventilation System," showing the SCAT air ventilation duct passing fairly close to the intake/exhaust flanges . . . enroute to the firewall and ultimately into the cabin area.

A couple of readers speculated that, in the event of an engine compartment fire, additional protection for the ducting and/or the 2 inch hole in the firewall might be needed. The suggestion has merit and the following suggestions are offered for builders who feel strongly about trying to completely fireproof the SCAT air ventilation installation shown or a similar one. You could:

1. Remove the ducting clamps adjacent to the cylinder intake/exhaust flanges and relocate the duct away from the exhaust flanges attachment area.

2. Wrap the SCAT duct with a fireproof tape or material.

3. Construct a stainless steel shutter at the firewall which you can manually close to seal off the engine

Shown here is a firewall air duct shut-off similar in concept to the drawing shown in the text. A simple stainless steel slide closes the air inlet in the firewall when "choke-like" control knob is pulled in the cockpit.

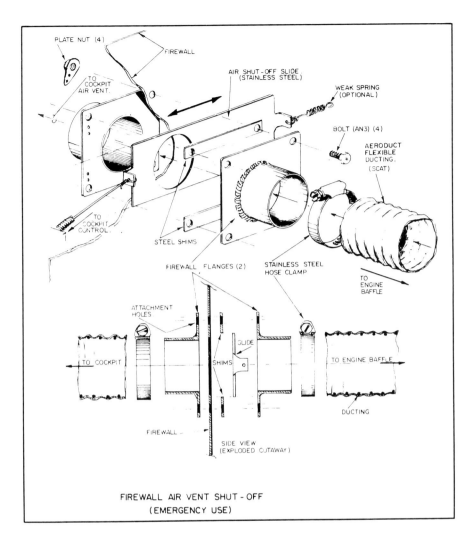

FIREWALL AIR VENT SHUT - OFF
(EMERGENCY USE)

A hollowed plywood jig was made to hold the stainless steel bowl in the upright position. The bowl, when inserted in the jig, should have about ¼" of its rim protruding above the plywood jig surface.

This shows how the steel bowl is clamped in the jig. The protruding edge of the bowl is then hammered down flat and drilled for riveting to the firewall.

2.

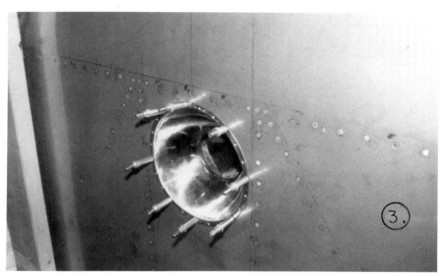

The stainless steel bowl recess is installed in the firewall and clecoed in preparation for riveting.

3.

compartment in the event of a fire. Refer to the drawing for details of this commonly used option.

Fortunately, a fire in the engine compartment is an uncommon occurrence.

When it does occur on the ground, it usually results from a flooded carburetor and a botched starting procedure.

When it occurs in flight, it is most frequently caused by a completely broken exhaust stack . . . most usually adjacent to the welded exhaust flange attachment. The exhaust pipe sags, or drops away, and the hot exhaust gases blast into the engine compartment. Ordinarily there is nothing flammable in the immediate area and a catastrophic fire will not immediately develop, however, a precautionary landing should be expedited.

This is not to say that an engine compartment fire cannot occur from a broken exhaust pipe. It can. Particularly if your engine is dirty and oil soaked. Oil on an engine can and will ignite readily and may develop into an intense fire . . . at least for as long as there is oil to feed the flames.

VULNERABILITY OF MATERIALS TO FIRE DEFINED

Most of us are aware that some materials burn readily, particularly if they get hot enough . . . others do not.

Do you know that the FAA has methodically defined the degrees of fire resistance or protection expected of different aircraft materials? These terms, briefly defined for your convenience, follow:

1. **Fireproof:** Stainless steel firewalls and steel engine mounts are deemed to be **fireproof.** Rather, the FAA says that any structure or materials capable of carrying their normal loads, and performing their design function satisfactorily, is considered to be **fireproof** IF they can withstand a flame of approximately 2000 degrees F. for 15 minutes . . . that's hot, man!

2. **Fire-Resistant:** When subjected to a flame (similar to that produced by a Bunsen burner) for 30 seconds, no penetration of the material should result. If, after the removal of the flame, the material does ignite, the flame should extinguish itself within 15 seconds with no smoldering or glowing visible 10 seconds later.

3. **Flame-Resistant:** When ignited by a flame, the

A rear view of the firewall recess as installed in a RV-6A. The insulation material was removed from around the stainless steel bowl to show off the installation details.

This is a much simpler method for modifying a stainless steel bowl. After the rolled edge has been ground off or cut away, tin snips are used to make radial cuts about ½" deep. The tabs are then bent down, drilled and riveted to the firewall as shown here.

material burn rate should not exceed four inches per minute. Alternatively, if the material does not support combustion after being exposed to a flame for 15 seconds, or if the flame extinguishes itself and the afterburn does not extend into the undamaged areas, the material is considered to be **flame-resistant.**

4. **Flash-Resistant:** Any material when ignited by a match, or similar means, is considered to be **flash-resistant** if the material, after a 15 second exposure to the flame, does not support combustion or **the burn rate does not exceed 20 inches per minute.**

Now you can use these terms like a pro when evaluating your test results on the insulation, fabrics, and carpeting for your airplane.

As for the aircraft materials and parts to be found in all aircraft, most of them are FAA rated by some Mil Spec — and their tolerances to temperature extremes are well documented.

Speculation has it that if an engine compartment fire were to burn long enough, just about all the engine compartment accessories would suffer serious damage or be destroyed by the flames.

Here's how the various materials and components installed in your engine compartment rate from the point of view of fire tolerance.

Except for the steel parts and components located in the engine compartment, most materials are not fireproof and cannot withstand the 2000 degree F. to 2800 degree F. flames likely to be encountered. Here's how vulnerable these materials are. They include:

Aeroquip 303 Fuel/Oil Hoses — up to 250 degrees F.
Aeroduct Flexible Ducting:
SCAT (red) — up to 450 degrees F.
CAT (black) — up to 350 degrees F.
Aircraft Wiring — 200 degrees F. to 300 degrees F.
Rubber grommets — flammable (a match flame will cause them to burn).
Fire Sleeves — up to 500 degrees F.
Aluminum Fittings — melt at 1100 degrees F.

IS YOUR FIREWALL FIREPROOF?

Your stainless steel firewall will withstand a flame of 2800 degrees F. before it begins to melt. An aluminum firewall? It would begin to melt at approximately 1200 degrees F. by definition that certainly is NOT a fireproof material.

But . . . and it is a big but . . . even a steel firewall cannot be regarded as being fireproof if flame (or carbon monoxide) is able to penetrate through one or more of the many holes and openings you may have had to make in the firewall.

ON SEALING THE FIREWALL

Obviously all firewall openings, no matter how small, must be properly sealed. How effective your sealing job is depends, for the most part, on the materials you used.

You may think you have done a good job of sealing the firewall because no light is visible (check with a flashlight) around any of the openings. But, will your sealing effort keep flames out of the cockpit in event of an engine compartment fire?

Yes, if you used steel firewall shields properly backed up with an asbestos type washer and, perhaps, a rubber grommet.

Otherwise the answer is NO, if you only used rubber grommets . . . and maybe some ordinary silicone adhesive smeared around the grommets. Plain ol' rubber grommets are not fireproof, nor are they fire resistant by any stretch of the imagination. They will burn when you put a match to them. Imagine how quickly a hot flame in the engine compartment would destroy all rubber grommet seals and allow flames to penetrate into the cockpit areas.

Using a special high temperature (red) silicone adhesive (Permatex, Dow Corning, etc.) over and around the grommets would improve their fire resistance considerably because that type of sealant is effective to temperatures up to 650 degrees F. It is not fireproof, of course, but it could buy the pilot time in event of an emergency situation.

How about the hoses? The fuel and oil hoses? The commonly used Aeroquip 303 hose, for example, has an operating temperature ranging from -65 degrees F. to 250 degrees F. Obviously, it wouldn't take long for the exhaust from a broken exhaust stack to burn through any nearby hose.

Keep your fuel lines as far away from exhaust stacks as is practical for this reason.

Naturally, your engine compartment fuel lines should be sleeved with Firesleeves. Their effectiveness in operating temperatures up to 500 degrees F. will help "fireproof" the installation.

Although a Firesleeve does not increase the operating limits of the 303 hose, it does protect the hose longer, and to a greater degree from a direct flame.

In the same manner, the flexible red ducting (SCAT), and the two ply SCEET ducting offer greater protection (up to 500 degrees F.) in the engine compartment than does the less expensive CAT (black) flexible ducting.

The best advice? Keep your engine compartment clean and check the exhaust system regularly for cracks.

Highly modified 0-200 engine in Formula One racer, Nemesis, perennial winner at Reno. The 4 to 1 exhaust system is visible here as is the 12 inch prop extension. Nemesis set a world record by averaging 277.25 mph at the Aeroshell Speed Dash competitions held at the 1993 EAA Oshkosh Convention.

The Effects of Engine Compartment Heat

DURING MID-AUGUST in Austin (Texas, that is), the temperatures hovered daily around 100° F and peaked out one day at 106° F. I flew my Emeraude that day. Man, was it hot! But the outdoor air was nowhere near as hot as that air rising out of the oil inspection door opening when I opened it after the flight. It got me to thinking about the problems that sort of heat had previously given me in my Rolls Royce powered installation (notice how I slipped in that ego bit?) and the precautions I had better take with my Falco engine installation.

Lately, a lot of builders have been learning that their new, high powered (anything over 100 hp), closely cowled airplanes seem to be developing more and more unexpected engine operation problems and other engine related problems. Welcome to the club.

Experienced builders and aircraft manufacturers alike have long been painfully aware that heat induced engine compartment problems were difficult to isolate and solve. Persistent instances of vapor lock in fuel systems, failures of magnetos, alternators (or generators) and, yes, even batteries and vacuum pumps, have often been traced to excessive localized engine compartment heat.

How hot it really gets in the engine compartment came to me as a surprise. I had never before thought

Can you imagine the amount of heat that battery is being subjected to? You're right, too much! The battery kept boiling over and lasted almost one year. An insulated deflector between the muffler and the battery has since been added. That helps but the battery could use a blast of cooling air.

in terms of specific temperatures outside of being subconsciously aware that it did get hot in there.

HOW HOT DOES IT GET?

Well, sir, if I am to believe what I see, it gets hot enough inside the engine compartment to boil water, or more to the point, fuel . . . and then some.

While prowling the flight line during Oshkosh '84, I came across an uncowled Lycoming engine installation that caught my eye. It had several Temperature Indicator Plates stuck on it in various places around the engine compartment (see photo). The builder had apparently been concerned with his temperatures at the firewall, fuel pump and at other strategic locations on the engine. An excellent idea. I'll bet he was surprised, though, to learn that most areas were recording searing temperatures of 340° F, higher in some places. Even if you challenge the accuracy of these readings, temperatures around 300° F are HOT.

TEMPERATURE MONITORS

Temperature monitors, under the trade name "TEMPIL," are available from BIG THREE INDUSTRIES, INC., 2901 Hamilton Blvd., South Plainfield, NJ 07080. Phone 201-757-8300.

Their product, "Tempilable," is ideally suited for homebuilders. The Tempilable is a non-reversible temperature indicator with a guaranteed accuracy of 1%.

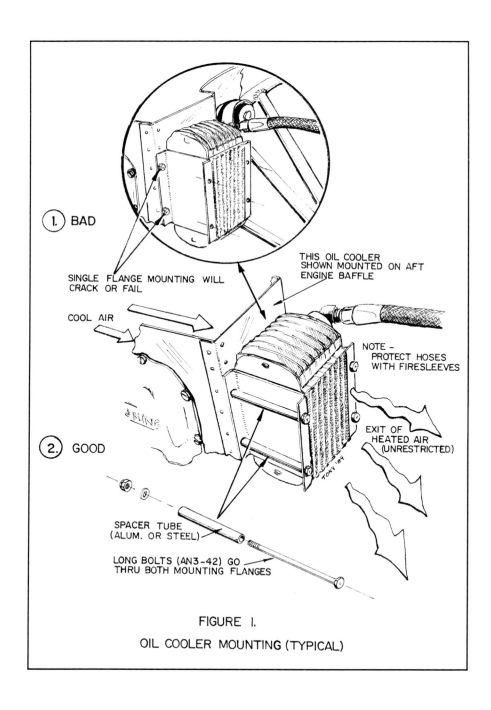

1. BAD

SINGLE FLANGE MOUNTING WILL CRACK OR FAIL

THIS OIL COOLER SHOWN MOUNTED ON AFT ENGINE BAFFLE

COOL AIR

NOTE - PROTECT HOSES WITH FIRESLEEVES

2. GOOD

EXIT OF HEATED AIR (UNRESTRICTED)

SPACER TUBE (ALUM. OR STEEL)

LONG BOLTS (AN3-42) GO THRU BOTH MOUNTING FLANGES

FIGURE I.

OIL COOLER MOUNTING (TYPICAL)

Above — Some Piper aircraft have a metal compartment that isolates the fuel pump and gascolator from the excessive heat of the engine compartment to reduce risk of vapor lock. 1. Protective compartment. 2. Fuel pump. 3. Flexible hose (radius too sharp). 4. Gascolator.

This fuel pump and gascolator are interconnected with flexible hoses protected by Firesleeves . . . good. The hose routing, however, could be improved by eliminating the sharp bends and vertical rises. Note the stickers affixed to the fuel pump and just to the left on the firewall. They are temperature indicators.

The self-adhesive backing permits simple installation and provides a temperature history you can remove and keep as a permanent record.

A similar product is the "Temp Plate Recorder" manufactured, under patent, by a company called WAHL of Los Angeles, CA.

Examples of this type of temperature monitor are visible in the photo accompanying this text.

The particular stickers illustrated apparently record temperatures from 310 degrees F, to 340 degrees F in 10 degree increments.

Each stick-on Temperature Indicator is fabricated with 4 small circular openings that will turn black at some pre-calibrated temperature. In checking several of the Temperature Indicator Plates, I could see that most of the circles labeled 340° F had turned black in that particular engine installation. Sure, that's hot. That seems very hot. I would assume, however, that during engine operations and flight, the temepratures are lower than that due to the constant flow of cooling air through the compartment. Still, there are always stagnant areas where the temperatures can easily

The arrow points to a metal tube conducting cooling air from the rear baffle to the left magneto. A similar vent tube is located to blast cool air on the right magneto also. Magnetos will fail if subjected to prolonged high temperatures.

A simple exhaust system but one that will generate a tremendous amount of heat in the engine compartment if a pressure cowling is installed. A similar installation in a Cub was no problem because the engine compartment was as ventilated as a breezeway.

Visualize all those long cross-over exhaust pipes being enclosed in a tight cowling. They generate a lot of heat in the bottom compartment of the engine that has to be coped with to keep engine temperatures within limits.

This installation shows how an oil cooler may be installed off the back baffle so that the hot air exiting the oil cooler is deflected downward to expedite its passage through and out of the engine compartment.

reach those mentioned. Besides that, an engine shutdown ends the flow of cooling air, and there is always a significant heat rise . . . until the engine finally cools down. Furthermore, temperatures in the 340° F range are easily reached and exceeded in areas adjacent to the exhaust pipes. These pipes radiate temperatures in the range of 1200° F, possibly higher.

Can you imagine what temperatures like that could do to your battery? To the fuel in your lines, pumps and gascolator? To the ducting and even to your hardware? And how about plastic tubes? When you think it all through, you begin to realize that most engine compartment problems are, indeed, heat related.

Almost any engine installation can be improved and benefit from a fresh review of its heat sensitive installations, so why not take another look at yours?

HEAT SENSITIVE MATERIALS

You have probably read that you should not use common fiber-insert type lock nuts (AN365) where they might be subjected to high temperatures. Now you know why they shouldn't be used in essential applications in the engine compartment. Since engine compartment temperatures often exceed 300° F, that is no place for a nut that is satisfactory for use only to temperatures not exceeding 250° F. Guess what can happen to the fiber locking feature. You should instead use the all-metal high temperature type nuts for all important

engine compartment installations.

How about ducting? You know they have that black (CAT) ducting and the red (SCAT) ducting. Not only is the price different, the temperatures each is capable of withstanding differs, too. The red ducting, capable of withstanding temperatures from -80° F to something over 450° F, costs about twice as much as the black ducting which cannot tolerate temperatures higher than 300° F. Be sure you are using the red stuff for your carburetor heat box ducts, the fuel injector air duct and any duct that is directly connected to a heat muff.

Well, need we say anything about plastic hoses and lines inside the engine compartment? I would not recommend their use outside of, perhaps, a vent line not directly exposed to a heat source. Certainly do not use a plastic hose for your engine breather line. Efficient venting of the engine is critical and you don't want some plastic hose collapsing and creating an awkward engine operational situation.

Most FAA inspectors will not approve the use of plastic hoses for fuel and oil lines. I know of one builder who was able to get the inspector to O.K. his installation by slipping a Firesleeve over the line. However, I don't know that that is such a good idea either.

HOT BATTERIES

Show me a hot battery and I will show you one that is not long for this world. Take a good look at the photo

109

This particular VW engine installation is typical of those seen in many low wing Sonerai homebuilts. Note that engine cooling is augmented by the automotive type oil cooler mounted on top of the engine.

showing the battery and huge muffler face to face. Can you imagine how much heat that battery is being subjected to? When a battery is exposed to temperatures much over 100°F, its longevity is jeopardized. (Incidentally, that one didn't last a year.)

A battery installed on the firewall in the engine compartment has a tough life. Unless ventilated, it will be subjected to the very high temperatures previously mentioned. These temperatures are sufficient to make the battery boil. Needless to say, the battery life then drops as precipitously as penny stocks in a bear market.

A battery mounted on the firewall can and should be vented by ducting air into the battery case. This is fine while the engine is operating and the aircraft is in flight. However, what happens after engine shutdown? It could take quite a bit of time for the trapped residual heat to drop below 100°F . . . all the while the battery is suffering the damaging effects of the heat.

HOT MAGNETOS (I MEAN REAL HOT!)

It has become a standard practice to "ventilate" the magnetos. Many a magneto and engine failure has

been charged directly to the malfunctioning of a magneto that had been operating in an environment too hot for it. That dead air space behind the baffles where both magnetos are situated becomes unbelievably hot.

A Cheerful Note: If you are building a pusher, like the VariEze or Long-EZ, you will be pleased to learn that engine compartment heat will not be much of a problem in your installation because accessories are, for the most part, located in an area of incoming cool air.

Most magnetos can function and more or less survive up to certain critical temperatures. I understand that the Slick magnetos, for example, fade away when temperatures reach approximately 270° F while the Bendix mags fare somewhat better and can tolerate temperatures of up to 350° F . . . for a time.

Directing a blast of cooling air over both magnetos, therefore, is essential to their longevity. Short ⅝" to 1" diameter tubes projecting from the rear baffle and aimed directly at each magneto will do much to keep your magnetos operating properly. Do not omit this provision in your installation.

This is one way to modify the back engine baffle for mounting a standard aircraft oil cooler.

Some may balk at the idea of bleeding air through the baffles and look on it as a wasteful, drag-producing inefficient thing to do. Maybe so, but I'd be willing to give a little if it will insure that my magnetos don't suffer a heat stroke . . . wouldn't you.

HOT ALTERNATORS (OR GENERATORS)

The cooling air blast tube for the magnetos works equally as well for an alternator or generator, wherever it may be located. Due to its location, however, ducting may have to be used to position the air outlet correctly. (Most generators have a small blast tube connection and all you need do is to connect it to a source of airflow with a length of ducting.) Be sure your alternator or generator does get its flow of cooling air even if you have to punch out another baffle opening. By now you may begin thinking that your baffling installation is becoming more like Swiss Cheese than the ideal installation you first visualized . . . sorry about that.

OIL COOLER

Continental engine installations (65 hp - 100 hp) do not need an oil cooler but Lycomings do. An oil cooler should be considered as mandatory for all Lycoming engines (O-235s, O-320s on up). It should be mounted properly (see photo and Figure 1) and located in an area where the air flow through the cooler is uninhibited. The oil cooler may be mounted up front in the inlet baffle (LHS) or in the rear baffle as shown. Some are even mounted on the firewall but require extensive ducting. At any rate, do not try to support the oil cooler with short bolts through only one of the flanges . . . it won't last.

The air exiting from the oil cooler will be hot and you should regard it as another unwelcome contributor to your engine compartment heat problem. Be sure that the hot air from the oil cooler doesn't blast directly on the gascolator or the auxiliary fuel pump, or for that matter, directly on a fuel line.

Oil cooler hoses should be protected with fire-sleeves. In this instance, you obviously are not trying to contain the heat in the hoses but are more concerned with safeguarding them in the event of an engine compartment fire.

EXHAUST SYSTEMS CONTRIBUTION

Here is a potential troublemaker. The sooner you

One builder's attempt to keep engine oil temperatures within limits involves mounting an automotive type oil cooler on top of the engine. An opening is cut in the back baffle to exit the hot air. Note the special louvers and case surrounding the radiator.

can dump the hot exhaust gases overboard, the less of a heat problem you will have. Hence, short stacks equate with no engine compartment heat problems. On the other end of the scale we have the crossover exhaust system. We all know that the crossover exhaust system is reputed to be the most efficient that can be installed. The penalty you must pay, however, may give you cause to reconsider.

A crossover system, while marvelously efficient, does concentrate a lot more heat in the engine compartment because of the extra lengths of pipe crammed inside the cowling. These pipes, in conducting the engine exhaust gases (temperatures up to 1200° F) through the engine compartment, pass in close proximity to: the cowling, causing it to blister; closely skirt the crankcase, raising the oil temperature even more; pass the engine mount closely, inviting localized corrosion and, in passing through the area occupied by the fuel pump and gascolator, raising their temperatures even higher.

A lot of crossover systems have some of the pipes almost touching the cowling causing it to blister and become burned. The usual fix is to wedge in an asbestos or fire-resistant blanket between the pipes and the cowling. Others resort to wrapping the exhaust pipes to form a heat shield. The best solution, of course, is to keep your cowling as far away from the hot pipes as possible. An inch clearance and a good flow of air would help solve that problem.

One last note. Do not brace exhaust pipes against the aircraft structure with a rigid brace. Use a strap that is shock mounted to allow for the engine's movement and vibration in its shock mounts. A broken exhaust pipe in an engine compartment is a very real fire hazard.

While you're at it, see what else needs protection from engine compartment heat. How about those wires . . . ?

"If it's not right, do it over."

IGNITION & ELECTRICAL ■ 7 ■

Minimizing Your Battery Problems

I have it all figured out. The way to avoid Gel/Cell battery problems is by installing a lead-acid battery, and the way to avoid lead-acid battery problems is by using a Gel/Cell. Come to think of it, if you want to avoid all battery problems, don't install either kind. How's that for problem solving?

GEL/CELL BATTERIES

It is well to remember that the Gel/Cell battery was not developed for the homebuilt market but for a larger one aimed at the golf cart set, wheel chair users and the recreational vehicle market.

I have been using Gel/Cell batteries for several years. My first battery lasted over a year. The second lasted almost two years. The third, only two months, and the last one just a bit past the "90 day" guarantee. This involvement with Gel/Cells has cost me, to date, almost $300 for batteries over a four year period. A number of local amateur builders have had somewhat similar but less costly experiences with their Gel/Cell batteries. So it seems that installing a Gel/Cell in your aircraft is a matter of "you pays your money and you takes your chance".

Still, if ever a battery was conceived for the home-builder, the Gel/Cell is it. It is perfectly suited for aer-obatic flight as it has no liquid electrolyte that can spill out when the battery is inverted. And, except for check-ing it for security of installation and keeping the termi-nals clean and tight, it is virtually maintenance free. The battery is "sealed" in that it cannot be opened and requires no servicing.

It does, however, have tiny vents, and corrosive fumes can still be vented, especially during periods of charging and discharging. This, in my estimation, means that installing the battery in the cockpit area without a battery box or some other sort of vented en-closure is not recommended.

A Gel/Cell battery that has been idle in an aircraft equipped with an electric clock and has, say, a com-puter memory current requirement as well, will ul-timtely (in two or three weeks) be drained of its stored energy.

When you finally get out to the airport again, the

The battery box has been modified so that it can be partially reces-sed in the battery compartment floor. This will improve accessibil-ity and permit the cells to be easily serviced with water as needed.

The same battery box recessed in the battery compartment floor. Ease of access is obvious. The wires are from a battery charger which is giving the new "dry charged" lead-acid a boost to fully charge it.

The high location on the firewall gets the battery away from most of the direct engine heat. However, a battery box should always be used with a lead-acid battery.

Here is what one manufacturer considers to be a proper battery installation. Note the drain tube at the bottom of the case.

battery will be dead. Then when you try to recharge the battery it may appear to be "open circuited," or you may find that it will not accept the normal amount of current when the charger is hooked up. All you can do is be patient and leave the charger connected . . . and hope.

Then, providing the battery hasn't failed internally, after a period of several hours it will ordinarily start to accept larger and larger amounts of current. This will continue until the normal fully charged current level is reached. If you are lucky, the battery should recover and thereafter accept normal recharges unless, of course, you again let it remain idle for a long period of time in a discharged state.

Never store a Gel/Cell battery, or for that matter a lead-acid battery, in a discharged condition. The risk is great that the battery will not respond to your attempts to recharge it.

I found that a Gel/Cell appears to operate most efficiently at somewhat higher voltage charging rates.

NOTE: It is easy to moniter the system voltage and battery condition when you have a voltmeter installed in your plane. On the other hand, an ammeter is more commonly installed but it doesn't tell you much, only that the system is charging or not. It cannot show that the voltage regulator/alternator team is producing the voltage your system needs . . . or that the battery is fully charged.

The manufacturer (Globe) of the Gel/Cell batteries used most by homebuilders recommends in their Charging Manual that a constant voltage-limited current charger be used for recharging their batteries (at 14.4 volts . . . maybe as high as 14.7 volts).

Since you can't get a hydrometer into one of these "sealed" batteries, another way to determine if the battery is fully charged is to moniter the battery charger needle. The battery will be fully charged once the current stays stabilized at a low level indication for a couple of hours or so.

THE LEAD-ACID AIRCRAFT BATTERY

A lead-acid aircraft battery is the most reliable choice you can make. A lead-acid aircraft battery, unlike the automotive type, has spill proof caps that automatically seal the cells when the battery is inverted. That makes the aircraft battery suitable for use in an aircraft that is only occasionally flip-flopped. (No, amigo, those no-spill caps will not fit an auto battery.) If your aircraft doesn't have an inverted oil and fuel system capability, the lead-acid aircraft battery is the most dependable one to use. It does require the installation of a battery case. However, as previously pointed out, a battery case installation is advisable regardless of whether a lead-acid battery or a Gel/Cell battery will be installed. Besides, you might want to be able to switch from one type of battery to another.

ACTIVATING A NEW LEAD-ACID BATTERY

Here is where many of us get off to a poor start (ugh!). We spend good money to buy a new battery, and all we do is yank out the old one, slip in the new battery, connect the terminals and away we go. I doubt if one out of three of us ever takes the time to read, or to abide by, the battery preparation and installation instructions.

Anytime you have to replace the battery, ask yourself, "Why?". Was it due to old age? If so, that was to be expected. On the other hand, did the battery fail because of a charging problem? If there is a charging problem, the new battery will also fail prematurely unless you correct the charging system malfunction.

115

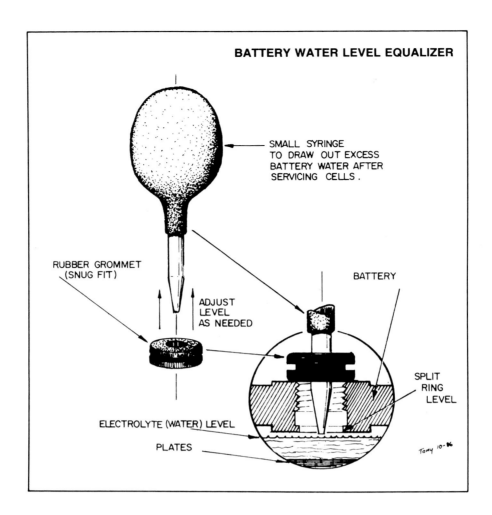

BATTERY WATER LEVEL EQUALIZER

SMALL SYRINGE TO DRAW OUT EXCESS BATTERY WATER AFTER SERVICING CELLS.

RUBBER GROMMET (SNUG FIT)

ADJUST LEVEL AS NEEDED

BATTERY

SPLIT RING LEVEL

ELECTROLYTE (WATER) LEVEL

PLATES

Tony 10-86

Most batteries received via UPS are "dry charged" and are accompanied with a plastic container packed along side containing the battery acid (electrolyte). Here's the basic procedure for activating a lead-acid battery properly.

Unpack the battery, the acid and read the instructions.

Manufacturers differ in the battery activation procedures recommended, but typically you will be instructed to remove the vent caps and remove or destroy any sealing device which is incorporated to seal the cell openings.

Next, they'll have you fill each cell of the battery with the electrolyte furnished.

NOTE: Some experts say all electrolytes are the same. The Gill battery people, however say differently, and they are not alone, I'd guess that the difference may only be in the proportions of sulfuric acid and water ratios they prefer for their battery to increase or decrease the specific gravity of the electrolyte. So, just to be sure, use only the electrolyte acid furnished with your battery.

You will need about two quarts so don't carelessly spill it. That plastic bag containing the battery acid can be tricky to handle. Be careful, too, not to splash any of the acid in your eyes or on your clothing. That stuff

eats holes in everything so don't dump the excess acid just anywhere.

Now, here is where many of us might go wrong. Fully charge your new battery at the rate specified, and not the way you assume would be all right.

There are those who say it is not necessary to charge a "dry charged" battery . . . just go fly it. Still others swear by a high booster amperage charge of about 25 amps for 10 minutes, while some say use a slow 3 ampere charge and continue charging until the specific gravity of the battery reaches a fully charged 1.240 or higher. So whose right? The correct recommendation is the one made by the manufacturer of your particular battery.

PERIODIC SERVICING IS ESSENTIAL

Your battery should be inspected and serviced periodically. By periodically, I mean at least once a month . . . every two weeks if you fly a lot. What does this involve? Not much. Would you believe about 10 minutes of your time?

1. Keep the top of the battery clean, the cables tight (very important) and the battery secure in its mount.

2. Add sufficient water, if needed, to bring the level up to the bottom of the split rings.

Never, ever, permit the electrolyte level to drop

116

The aft location just behind the canopy skirt will make this battery easily accessible when the aircraft is completed. However, the battery compartment is small and the battery is tall, making it difficult to inspect and service.

This is the same aircraft but the battery was recessed to enable easy inspection and maintenance of the cells. Builder obviously is concerned that he might accidentally reverse polarity when connecting an external power source to the aircraft.

problem. And you can't imagine why anyone would get upset over a little thing like having a dead battery. After all, some guys have to hand prop their little sportplanes before every flight — and think nothing of it.

Although manual starts may be routine for them, it is only because they are experienced and they and their aircraft are well prepared for such a procedure.

That may not be so for the gent who is more skilled in flipping a switch than he is in flipping a prop. He, like most pilots today, probably has had little or no experience in hand propping an engine. If so, he should not even think about doing so unless:

1. He has an experienced individual in the cockpit who can stand on the brakes and be ready to retard that throttle the second the engine starts.

2. He has parking brakes he can set. Even so, he should chock the wheels . . . or tie the tail down.

3. He has propped a plane before.

Naturally, there are all sorts of situations which make simple rules not worth the paper they are written on.

For example, if you are alone on some remote airstrip with a dead battery, what are you going to do?

That's right, you'll probably try to get the engine started by propping it yourself. You had better be extra careful, though, and at the very least chock the wheels with rocks, and strap the control stick (wheel?) back with the safety belt, if you can. Then, check and check again that the throttle is not open too far.

Understandably, this is a last ditch type of assault on an unexpected problem.

After the engine starts, your troubles may not yet be over. The engine will be operating nicely on magneto power. But if the battery was really dead, it will not have had any power for activating the battery solenoid and the battery circuit. This means that the excitation of the alternator field will not take place, nor will the alternator start recharging the battery, no matter how long you run the engine. Your electrical system will still be "kaput".

Don't wait until you have a dead battery. Figure out, beforehand, a safe practical way to get your engine started in spite of a weak or dead battery.

Your contingency plan should also include a means for recharging the battery. Consider all the options afforded by various external power sources that might be available to you.

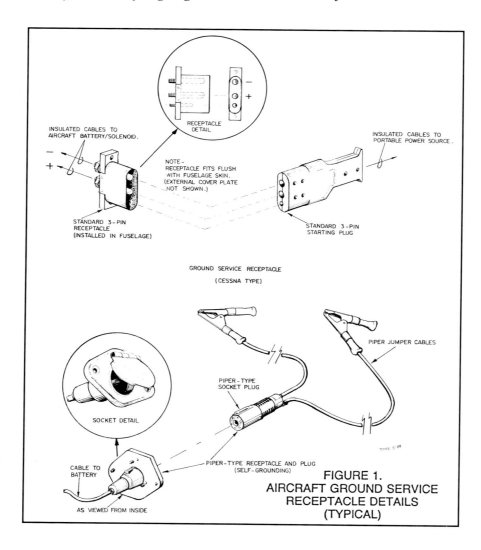

FIGURE 1.
AIRCRAFT GROUND SERVICE
RECEPTACLE DETAILS
(TYPICAL)

FIRST AID FOR THE BATTERY

Maybe the battery is not dead; maybe it's just wounded and only needs to be resuscitated.

When you turn on the master switch and hear the click of the battery solenoid, you know that the battery does have some life in it.

If you have a voltmeter installed, you can confirm this because it will immediately show you the battery voltage. It is most unlikely that your voltmeter will ever show much over 12 volts with the engine not running (even with a fully charged battery). But, if you see that the gauge is indicating hardly any voltage at all, you guessed it — at the very best all you can expect would be a few feeble starting grunts when the battery tries to zap the starter.

THE JUMP START TECHNIQUE

I'll bet just about everyone has had to "jump start" a car on occasion. If you fly long enough, the law of averages will, most likely, present you with the opportunity to try the jump start technique on whatever airplane you happen to be flying at the time.

Unfortunately, it is not as easy to jump start an airplane engine. Usually the airplane battery is not readily accessible.

Often, to get at the battery, you may have to remove the cowling, an access panel, or even the baggage compartment floor. Without a few tools at your disposal you could be out of luck.

When the battery is installed in an engine compartment battery box mounted on the firewall, messing with the battery could be very dangerous. The problem stems from the proximity of that lethal propeller just two feet away.

If you do have to remove the cowling, remember to move both it and the battery cover a safe distance away from the slipstream area of the starting engine.

There is, also, the very real risk that you could damage your electrical system and avionics should you accidentally, inadvertently, stupidly, or otherwise reverse the polarity with the jumper cables, even momentarily, as you attach them to the aircraft battery. By reversing polarity, I mean hooking the positive cable, unthinkingly, to the negative side and vice versa.

Your external power source for jump starting can be a vehicle, another battery, a battery charger plugged into a 115-120 volt wall plug somewhere or, preferably, an airport auxiliary power unit (APU) designed for such an operation.

But access to any or all of those external power sources won't help much if you can't get at your battery terminals.

THE GROUND SERVICE RECEPTACLE

If you are flying a store bought airplane, it may have, as optional equipment, a built-in ground service receptacle (located somewhere on the fuselage) where the manufacturer has provided a convenient point for connecting an external power source to the aircraft's electrical system. According to the aircraft manufacturers, ground service receptacles are most frequently installed for use in cold weather starting.

The main drawback to any external ground service receptacle is that it can accept only one type of connector plug. Unless the external power source cables are fitted with the correct type of plug, getting a boost start may be difficult (see Figure 1).

Unfortunately, this sort of complication can arise because some aircraft ground service receptacles and power source plugs differ in design.

Most Cessnas use one kind of three pronged plug, while Pipers utilize a single self-grounding cylindrical type. Of course, you would expect most attended airports to have a couple sets of power cables wired with the appropriate type plugs.

But don't count on it.,

So, if you are toying with the idea of installing a ground service receptacle in your homebuilt, think

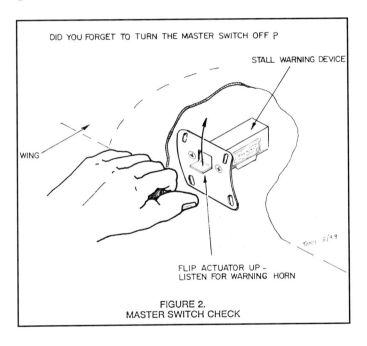

DID YOU FORGET TO TURN THE MASTER SWITCH OFF ?

STALL WARNING DEVICE

WING

FLIP ACTUATOR UP –
LISTEN FOR WARNING HORN

FIGURE 2.
MASTER SWITCH CHECK

again. It might only be rarely used and not worth the trouble to install.

In a general sense, an externally accessible battery terminal could be more useful than a conventional ground service receptacle . . . especially if your battery is buried somewhere in the aircraft where its battery terminals are not readily accessible from the ground. Useful, that is, because such an installation would provide a convenient place for attaching jumper cables, and you wouldn't have to rely on a particular type of power plug being available.

Remember, there will always be that reversed polarity risk previously mentioned any time you use such a set up to get a boost start or to recharge the battery.

Retraction tests and limit switch adjustments take time and if your gear is an electric one, could easily run the battery down without the added boost you can get from a plugged in battery charger.

You simply have to be extra careful.

The aircraft manufacturer installed ground service receptacles are generally wired so the aircraft's electrical system is protected from an inadvertent reverse polarity hook up.

However, some builders consider it adequate to run an automotive battery cable from the plus terminal of the battery to some area in the airplane that can be easily reached from the ground with a jumper cable. This stub battery cable extension could terminate near an opening in the cowling or perhaps somewhere in the cockpit area out of sight and out of the way.

Ready made automotive battery cables may be obtained in long lengths if needed.

When not in use, be sure to protect the free end of the terminal with a rubber boot or cover of some sort.

To use your extended stub battery terminal, connect the red (plus) jumper cable from an external power source to the free end of the cable in the aircraft, and the black jumper to a good aircraft ground, i.e., one of the exhaust stacks.

You can even use a battery charger as an external power source for jump starting the engine provided you have a hangar with an electrical outlet . . . and a long extension cord.

A battery charger is also handy for providing extra current to the battery while extensive maintenance of the electrical system is underway. Retraction tests and limit switch adjustments take time and, if your gear is an electric one, could easily run the battery down without the added boost you can get from a plugged in battery charger. Here again, be extra careful that you

don't accidentally reverse the polarity when hooking up the jumper cables.

SOLAR CHARGERS

A solar charger is no longer a science fiction sort of device. It has been proven quite practical in a number of homebuilts as a way to keep the battery charged. Of course, this is assuming the aircraft is often parked on the line or is flown regularly during daylight hours.

A single solar panel measuring about 4 inches by 12 inches can produce up to 70 milliamps, 15 volts and 1 watt, depending on the intensity of the sunlight striking the solar panel.

Since your electrical system is inactivated when you turn the master switch off, you would need to connect the solar panel directly to the battery. Or you could tie it into the electric clock wire if the wire has sufficient capacity. Of course, this solar trickle charge idea is not practical for the airplane that sits in the hangar for several weeks at a time.

Solar panels are extremely durable and could well last the life of the aircraft so there is no reason why it couldn't be left plugged into the aircraft's electrical system permanently.

These solar panels have a blocking diode which prevents current feed back. Otherwise, your battery could drain during cloudy days and during the long night time hours.

Incidentally, you can buy a solar panel for just under $50 from one of the larger homebuilt suppliers if you want to do a bit of experimentation.

12 Volts vs 24 Volts

The letter posed this question . . . "Which electrical system should I install in my Glasair? A 12 volt system or a 24 volt system?"

Which system do you think I recommended as being the better one to install in his homebuilt? (I'll give you a clue. I'm prejudiced in favor of the 12 volt system.)

Actually, either system will do a good job of operating all the accessories, lights, bells and buzzers he could cram into his airplane. Furthermore, either system will function equally as well under IFR conditions should the aspiration to operate in that realm appeal to him.

And, for good measure, I might have added that both the 12 volt and the 24 volt system are reliable. The difference in reliability, if any, most often appears to

be in the quality of the individual electrical components installed for that particular system.

If all this is true, what difference does it really make which system he chooses to install? I guess from a functional point of view there is no difference . . . certainly no visible difference. He couldn't, for example, look at an airplane and say, "That one looks like it has a 24 volt system."

To be honest about it, I can't tell by looking at electrical accessories and components which of them must operate on 12 volts and which on 24 . . . not without peeking at the data plates, I can't.

Having demonstrated my impartiality to this point, let's get down to the nitty gritty of the title subject. But,

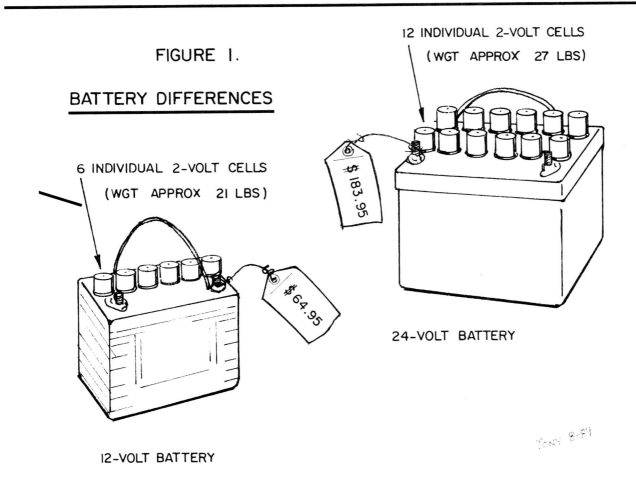

FIGURE I.

BATTERY DIFFERENCES

6 INDIVIDUAL 2-VOLT CELLS
(WGT APPROX 21 LBS)

$64.95

12-VOLT BATTERY

12 INDIVIDUAL 2-VOLT CELLS
(WGT APPROX 27 LBS)

$183.95

24-VOLT BATTERY

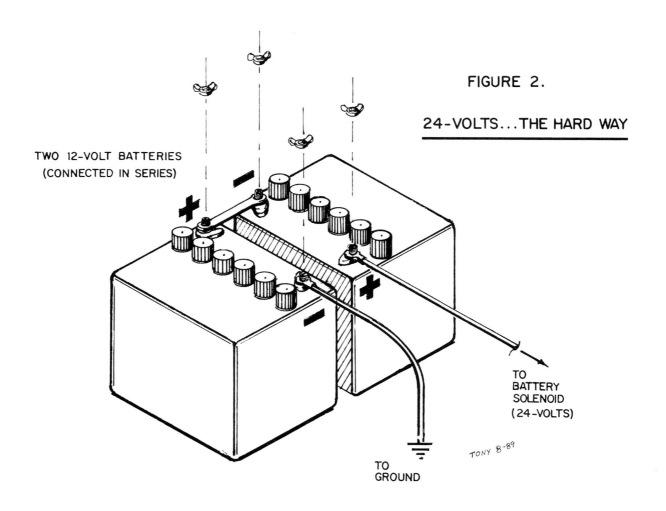

TWO 12-VOLT BATTERIES
(CONNECTED IN SERIES)

FIGURE 2.

24-VOLTS...THE HARD WAY

TO
BATTERY
SOLENOID
(24-VOLTS)

TONY 8-89

TO
GROUND

---

before going any further, we need to reach a common understanding of the electrical terms we will be evaluating.

WHEN ARE 12 VOLTS 14 VOLTS . . . AND 24 VOLTS 28 VOLTS?

Confused? Some builders are. However, the explanation is quite simple.

An aircraft's electrical system has its origin in the storage battery installed primarily for starting the engine and for serving as an initial power source for the aircraft's electrical system. This chemically stored power source (the battery) can be either a 12 volt battery or a 24 volt battery.

After the engine is started, its companion alternator (or generator), installed to supplement and replenish the battery voltage expended in starting the engine, normally cuts in and provides all the electrical power needed in flight.

The power generated by the alternator/generator is controlled and limited by a voltage regulator. This regulator permits the excess voltage produced by the alternator to go to and charge the battery, thereby replenishing its stored capacity.

The voltage regulator is set at approximately 14

volts for the 12 volt battery installation, and for 28 volts when a 24 volt battery is installed. Because of this, most of us sometimes call it a 12 volt system, and at other times a 14 volt system. The same is true of the 24/28 volt system.

In either instance, the larger number represents the approximate controlled voltage limit permitted by the regulator.

SELECTING AN ELECTRICAL SYSTEM

As I see it, the choice is simple to make.

1. If you already have an engine, look at its alternator (or generator) and starter. If these are 12 volt units, go with the 12 volt system . . . unless you are willing to replace them. They would be very expensive to replace with 24 volt units.

2. If you don't have an engine as yet, look over the instruments, radios and other accessories you may have already accumulated — and let them influence your choice.

But, what if you have both 12 volt and 24 volt stuff on hand that you would like to install? What then?

I think in almost every instance the 12 volt system would be your best option.

One thing is certain. Do not even entertain the

thought that you will solve anything simply by having both systems on board. You can do that, of course, but then you will have a hybrid electrical system that is going to be more complicated, more expensive, and heavier than either of the two systems would have been alone.

This means you would have to start with a 24 volt battery, or two 12 volt batteries connected in series — this dual 12 volt battery arrangement may be found in some Cessna 310s (see Figure 2). You would also have to find a way to step down the voltage for the 12 volt equipment.

Incidentally, the dual battery idea is not a good one unless you need ballast somewhere. You should realize that two 12 volt batteries will weigh approximately 42 pounds while a single 24 volter will only weigh about 27 pounds . . . and don't forget there is the added weight of another battery box to think about.

THE 28 VOLT SYSTEM . . . ITS GOOD POINTS

What are the touted advantages of a 28 volt system over those of a 14 volt system? There are not many, apparently.

Most of the local maintenance people I have talked to can only identify one generally acknowledged attribute. And that is that a 24 volt system can help you save weight by permitting the use of lighter wire gages for the aircraft's electrical system.

This is possible because the more powerful 24 volt system has the advantage of requiring less current to accomplish the same job, thereby allowing the use of the smaller and lighter wiring.

Had the weather been cooler at the time I asked them, some of these Texas acclimated maintenance types would probably have remembered to remind me of another advantage. Namely, that a 24 volt battery can produce a more spritely starting torque in the engine
. . . especially during cold weather. This capability could conceivably ease the cold weather electrical problems most commonly associated with the 12 volt systems — low battery voltage.

WHY STAY WITH THE 12 VOLT SYSTEM?

The 12 volt system has been used in virtually all light aircraft since electrical systems first came into being.

Here's what bothers me. If the 12 volt system has been a suitable installation for most single engine and light twin aircraft for all these many years, why would anyone even consider changing to the so-called "new" 28 volt system?

Our familiar 12 volt status quo was jolted when Cessna, back in 1979 or thereabouts, decreed that, henceforth, all of its production aircraft would be equipped with the 28 volt system.

Yes, this change would also include their "bottom of the line" single engined Cessna 150s (152).

As the acknowledged leader in the production of single engine aircraft, Cessna exercised its considerable influence in making the switch and many experts freely predicted that all aircraft would ultimately be equipped with the "superior" 24/28 volt system.

DISADVANTAGES OF THE 24 VOLT SYSTEM

I'm sure the average homebuilder views the claimed advantages somewhat differently than do the manufacturers who embrace the 28 volt system as progress. For instance:

1. For the homebuilder, one thing is immediately apparent. The 24 volt system is more expensive to install. It may not be more complicated, or much heavier, but it IS expensive to install. Very expensive.

2. I'm sure that a change to the 28 system will not result in any significant weight saving by using smaller gage wiring in our homebuilts . . . after all, how many feet of wiring is involved?

For that matter, I wonder if the manufacturers themselves will be able to save additional weight by switching to even lighter wire gages. Hasn't their wiring already been engineered to the minimum acceptable sizes (see Figure 3 — wire selection chart)?

To use the chart (Figure 3) for selecting the correct wire size for a particular circuit, you need to know:

1. The length the wire has to be.
2. The number of amps of current it is to carry.
3. Whether the current carried will be intermittent or continuous and whether the wire is single or bundled.

You will find that the wire lengths in your homebuilt are quite short and the current loads generally light . . . almost all of them less than 10 amps.

Using the chart and the values for the 14 volt system, let's select the correct size for a single wire that will be 15 feet long and carry a continuous current of 6 amps.

1. Find the diagonal line for 6 amps and follow it down to where it intersects the horizontal line number 15 in the 14 volt column (wire length).

2. From that intersection drop downward to the bottom of the chart to find the correct conductor size. The wire size falls between 18 and 16. In such split decisions, always select the larger gage wire size . . . 16 gage in this example.

Using the same example, check to see what size wire would be recommended if this were a 24 volt system. Checking where the 6 amp diagonal intersects the number 15 in the 24 volt column, drop down and read the recommended wire size. Notice that it runs off the chart around the 20 gage point.

Obviously, there wouldn't be much difference, weightwise, between a 16 gage and a 20 gage wire in such short lengths. The weight saving with a 24 volt system is more significant for long lengths because, generally, the wire size can be about 2 gages smaller than that required for a 12 volt installation.

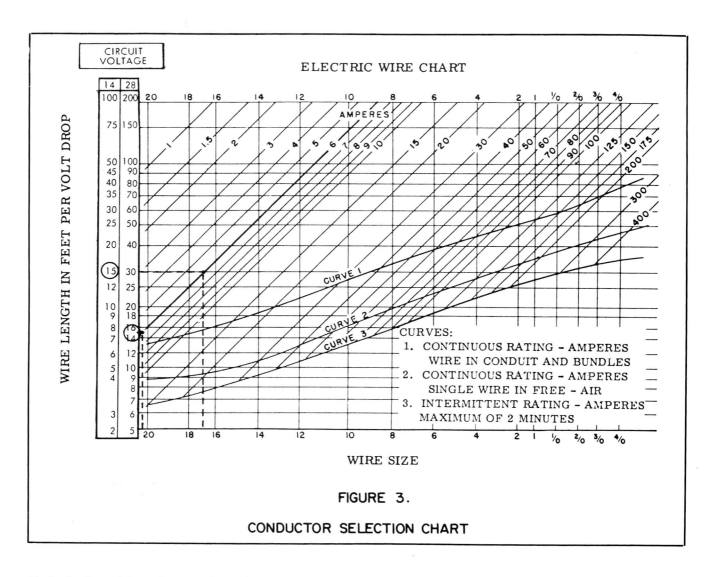

FIGURE 3.

CONDUCTOR SELECTION CHART

Technically, wiring sizes can be reduced to a point where they become more difficult to fabricate and too fragile to withstand handling in day to day service.

Most certainly, the average light single engined aircraft doesn't have too much wiring anyway . . . not like a 747 with its miles and miles of wiring and cable. Now, that's where the total weight reduction could be very important.

As for easier starting? . . . that is a subjective call. If an aircraft engine starts easily enough with a 14 volt system, how much easier would it have started with a 28 volt battery? In severe cold weather operations, the aircraft engines are preheated anyway.

I don't think the switch to a 28 volt system was very popular, or welcomed, by many of the avionics and parts departments around the country because it increased their inventory requirements. They would, henceforth, have to supplement their 14 volt stocks by adding duplicate 28 volt accessories . . . or, at least, more of them. This certainly would increase their cost of doing business by tying more money up in slow moving inventories.

FUTURE OUTLOOK

Will the 24 volt system become the inevitable future standard for light aircraft, and homebuilts as well?

In my opinion, no. Not during the next decade, at any rate.

The virtual collapse of single engine light plane production was a dismal development that really, really threw a monkey wrench into the grand idea of converting the aviation community to the 28 volt system.

As production declined, the anticipated thousands of 24 volt equipped single engined aircraft never materialized.

As we all know, costs are generally determined by quantities produced. And since large numbers of 24 volt accessories would not be required or be manufactured, guess what's been happening to their prices?

Here is another observation you can think about. With a smaller 28 volt aircraft fleet, fewer of the aircraft will ultimately end up in aircraft salvage yards. This means that even fewer used 24 volt parts will become available for the economy minded homebuilders and aircraft owners alike. These scarce components and accessories are already overpriced and the future outlook is even less encouraging.

WHAT ABOUT RADIOS AND AVIONICS EQUIPMENT?

Most radios and other avionics equipment advertised in Trade-A-Plane and elsewhere were manufactured for use in 14 volt installations. This means that when you order a radio or some accessory, a 12 volt unit will probably be shipped unless you specifically ordered a 24 volt version of the unit.

Fortunately, the prices are, in most instances, the same for 24 volt radios as they are for the 12 volters . . . but you must always remember that you may have to specify your 24 volt requirement, if you have one.

Here is something else to think about. Transponders are made to operate on 12 volt systems. Should you want to use one of them in an aircraft having a 24 volt system installed, you would have to install a dropping resistor. This can be done with transponders without experiencing any trouble because they have a constant current draw.

On the other hand, using a dropping resistor is not possible with aircraft radios because they have such a wide current operating range that you have to regulate the current at its source. This means you would have to install a power convertor to change the 24 volts to 14 volts. More costs are more weight. What does a power converter cost? About a couple of hundred bucks I am told.

Automobiles are equipped with 12 volt electrical systems and utilize a number of very reliable components and accessories that have been used by homebuilders in their aircraft for years. These include alternators, voltage regulators, fuel pumps, air filters and starters, to name a few. This valuable, economically priced source would no longer be usable by any builder who elects to install a 24 volt system.

Even in everyday operations, the 24 volt system could be a handicap. For example, what do you do when you have a dead battery? That's right . . . get a jump start.

This is easy enough to obtain when you have a 12 volt system because almost any vehicle can provide the 12 volt boost needed.

But, on the other hand, with that 24 volt battery installed, you would have to find a 24 volt power source somewhere. Maybe somebody will have a 28 volt APU . . . if you're lucky.

Pretty much the same situation arises when you want to charge your 24 volt battery in the hangar. Of

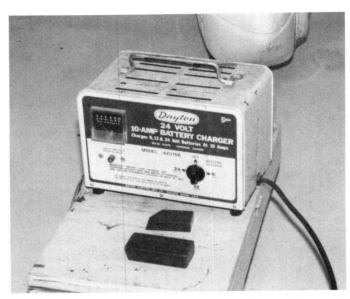

With a 24-volt system, jump starts will become impossible to get unless you can find a power source having 24-volts . . . that eliminates Volkswagens, Toyotas, etc. Furthermore, you will have to buy a more expensive 24-volt battery charger . . . just in case.

course, you'd buy a more expensive charger that could handle all kinds of voltages. But, chances are, if you're like most of us, you already own an inexpensive 12 volt battery charger.

Finally, maybe only the folks flying aerobatic type homebuilts or those who have to have a battery located in the cockpit area really care — but have you ever seen a 24 volt Gel Cell battery?

I don't know about you, but I've convinced myself that the 12 volt system is the only practical one for my RV-6 project.

"I thought I did."

Your Alternate Battery Choice

(The Gelled Electrolyte Battery)

Many homebuilders who have used or are using a sealed immobilized electrolyte battery (a gelled cell type, that is) are quite vocal in their support or condemnation of these batteries. And yet, even those who do not think highly of them are most reluctant to change back to the old lead acid (wet cell) aircraft batteries.

That odd acceptance is enough to make anyone who has never used such a battery to wonder why. Let's see if we can't shed some light on the nature of the gelled cell battery that would justify such a less than enthusiastic acceptance.

WHAT IS A SEALED IMMOBILIZED ELECTROLYTE BATTERY?

What we homebuilders refer to, generically, as a "gel cell battery" is in reality leaning a bit on the registered trademark of the Globe Company's Gel/Cell® battery.

Technically, we are talking about "an immobilized electrolyte battery" (admittedly, a most cumbersome term) . . . in other words, a gelled electrolyte type of battery.

As I understand it, the gelled electrolyte technology was first developed in Germany some years ago. Since then, the concept of sealing an immobilized electrolyte in a case has led to the development and refinement of rechargeable maintenance-free batteries.

These sealed, non-spill batteries were found to be an ideal source for all kinds of portable power applications. The electronics industry is finding a myriad of uses for these sealed rechargeable batteries. These compact power sources have found wide acceptance for use in wheel chairs, portable test equipment and, yes, in aerobatic airplanes, too — so there must be plenty of good reasons for their growth in popularity.

THE GELLED TYPE BATTERY'S BETTER FEATURES

1. The battery is constructed around a sealed immobilized (gelled) electrolyte which permits the battery to be installed and operated in any position. You could even install it upside down — but that would be kind of stupid. Unlike the liquid electrolyte found in lead acid wet cell batteries, there is no danger of the gelled electrolyte ever leaking out.

2. The typical sealed gelled cell battery is absolutely maintenance-free.

3. Obviously, this is THE battery to use in aerobatic aircraft . . . perhaps in most any homebuilt aircraft for that matter.

4. These batteries have a long shelf life. This minimizes the risk of buying a battery that has lost much of its capacity while on the dealer's shelf.

5. The average gelled electrolyte battery is compact and fairly light for its electrical capacity. Well, no heavier than a similar wet cell battery. For example, my present battery, a Sonnenschein (made in Germany), is a 12 volter with a 32AH capacity and weighs 22.5 lbs.

6. Regulations permit the shipment of these batteries by parcel post, UPS or by air without the need for special precautions or packing so they must be safe.

7. You can install this type of sealed battery in the cockpit area with no danger of suffering a corrosive acid spill or the presence of explosive gasses. For example, the Globe Gel/Cell® battery features patented self-resealing vents which prevent high pressures from building during charging.

Incidentally, the first of the gelled cell batteries to become generally available to homebuilders was the Globe Gel/Cell® battery . . . and that was not too many years ago.

I first saw one displayed in an EAA sales booth during an annual EAA Convention at Oshkosh and again later at a Sun 'n Fun Fly-In.

Since then these batteries have become a popular alternative to the old wet cell types. Their price is competitive, too (approximately $75 to $114).

As a result, the gelled batteries are becoming better known and more plentiful . . . they have not become cheaper, mind you, but are now much easier to locate.

For example, you can even order a gelled electrolyte type battery from your Sears catalog.

Naturally, not all gelled electrolyte batteries are alike, nor are all brands equal in capacity and reliability. You should be aware that most of these batteries were and are being manufactured for non-aircraft applications like standby power, communications equipment, golf carts and other high tech applications. It is not surprising, therefore, that some batteries may not have performed well in the more demanding aviation environment.

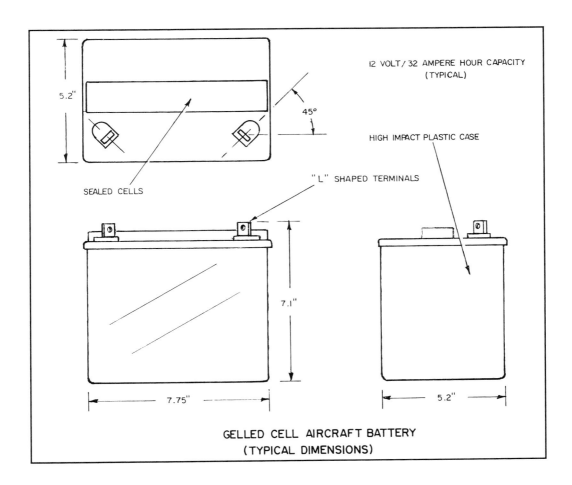

12 VOLT / 32 AMPERE HOUR CAPACITY
(TYPICAL)

HIGH IMPACT PLASTIC CASE

"L" SHAPED TERMINALS

SEALED CELLS

GELLED CELL AIRCRAFT BATTERY
(TYPICAL DIMENSIONS)

However, it is encouraging to note that aviation oriented manufacturers, including a few well known battery companies, are now producing or selling gelled electrolyte batteries for aircraft use under their own brand names.

THE BATTERY'S PHYSIQUE

The gelled cell batteries used by homebuilders are fairly standardized as to size, weight and capacity. This is important because . . . who wants a battery that won't fit the location or battery box already installed?

The size of the typical 12 volt gelled electrolyte battery is **approximately** 7-3/4" long by 5-1/4" wide and 7-1/4" in height.

Weight averages range between 21 and 23 pounds for the 12 volt batteries.

Note: A variety of smaller, lighter, rechargeable gelled cell batteries are also available. These may be of particular interest to builders who fly homebuilts without electrical systems.

The "standard" 12 volt gelled cell battery has two "L" shaped terminals to which the battery cables are connected with 5/16" bolts using a lock washer and a plain nut. I prefer the use of wing nuts because they help control that homebuilder tendency to over-tighten everything . . . battery connections included. Battery post connections should be clean and tight but not so tight you twist the terminal post off.

The earlier standard sized batteries had a 28 amp/hour capacity but the currently favored units now feature a 32 amp/hour capacity.

Construction of the battery and case is such that it is highly resistant to shock and vibration. The case is made of a non-conductive high impact plastic that will not deteriorate.

The battery is sealed and neither water nor electrolyte will ever have to be added. Indeed, your battery will be ready for use the minute that you receive it . . . and, happily, without first having to fill it with electrolyte, or to charge the thing.

INSTALLING YOUR GELLED ELECTROLYTE BATTERY

Absolutely no special preparations or requirements exist in this regard. a separate battery box is not essential although the battery can be better secured in one.

I am most familiar with the Globe Gel/Cell® battery as I have owned several of them through the years. The battery can be safely installed in a cockpit environment because it is sealed and its case is electrically non-conductive.

Note: The Globe battery folks do point out that care should be taken to ensure adequate ventilation . . . especially towards the end of a charging cycle and in

This metal battery box will house a sealed gelled electrolyte battery. Note the location is in the cockpit area adjacent to the firwall.

the case of an overcharge. At these times, especially under an overcharge condition, hydrogen and oxygen gas is dissipated into the atmosphere. If allowed to accumulate in a confined area and a spark is introduced, an explosion might result. Therefore, some provision for ventilation and air circulation within the battery enclosure during recharge is advisable . . . I am sure this advice could apply as well to most other gelled electrolyte brands.

I can report, however, that I have never detected any fumes or battery odors from my gelled electrolyte battery installation in the RV-6. The battery is mounted up front . . . in the cockpit . . . in a metal case.

Although the battery case is far from being air tight, I would certainly remove the battery from the aircraft should it ever need to be completely recharged.

Before you try to install your battery in the aircraft, take the precaution of taping the terminal posts with masking tape to prevent inadvertent shorting against the aircraft structure or some nearby metal component.

After the battery is in place and secured, remove the tape from the plus (+) terminal and connect the positive cable to it first. **Then** connect the ground cable to the negative (-) post. The battery ground cable or grounding strap should be connected directly to the engine or to some heavier metal structure.

Double check and assure yourself that your connections are correctly made and that you didn't accidentally reverse the polarity by connecting the first cable to the wrong terminal post. This could damage your solid state gadgets when the master switch is turned on, and would undoubtedly blow your alternator diodes into oblivion.

WHY BATTERIES FAIL

I suppose most battery problems, with the exception

of those resulting from old age, are aggravated by a poor installation and improper charging.

There is no reason why any aircraft battery cannot last 3 to 4 years . . . this includes the gelled electrolyte types, too. And yet I, like a number of other builders, have had my share of premature battery failures. I now wonder if all of the failures were the battery's fault.

I had one gelled electrolyte battery fail after 91 days. One did better than that. It only lasted 13 months. Another went 22 months before it started to ail. One was still going strong when I sold the airplane 3 years later. Either my electrical installation was improving or the batteries were getting better.

My current gelled cell battery is now 9 months old and is in excellent condition in spite of some heavy cranking and recharging last winter.

Friends and acquaintances tell of similar experiences. Past performance would indicate that some batteries (gelled types) last a long time while a few others fail completely in less than a year, or refuse to take and hold a charge.

It is difficult to sort out the reason or reasons for poor battery performance.

I know, for example, the 91 day wonder that failed was bought locally from a golf cart dealer. I suspect that particular battery had been on his shelf for a couple of years or more. As I recall, when the battery quit it would not hold a charge. I think, in this case, my voltage regulator was an accessory before and after the fact.

You can expect your idle battery to lose about 3% of its capacity per month at room temperature, and much more at 95-100 degrees F. I understand some idle batteries have been known to lose as much as 25% the first month.

I remember that one of my short lived batteries was

Arrow indicates the proximity of the exhaust system muffler . . . a heat producer. A battery located in the engine compartment may suffer from a shortened service life. Neither wet cell nor gelled batteries tolerate heat very well.

one that I had mounted on the firewall in the engine compartment just about 6 inches away from the hot end of a large Cessna type muffler. I guess that one ultimately died of heat prostration, and the abuse it received from a poorly adjusted automotive voltage regulator that kept feeding the battery 14 + volts whether the battery needed it or not.

There is nothing wrong with using a properly adjusted automotive voltage regulator. They are inexpensive, light in weight, and simple to install. Furthermore, some of them are now solid state units and may even be temperature compensated.

Keep this in mind. The voltage regulator's sole duty is to keep the battery fit and happy. It should be installed near the battery in the same temperature environment. Neither the battery nor the voltage regulator likes a hot environment.

KEEPING YOUR BATTERY HAPPY

My earlier battery systems did not include an over voltage regulator, hence the battery had no protection from an excessive charging rate that a faulty voltage regulator may sometimes impose on an already fully charged battery.

How the battery is being charged does affect its longevity and performance.

In this regard, an ammeter can help you keep tabs on your battery's condition. All you need to do is install a simple ammeter. One that reads - 30 - 0 - + 30, without other calibrations will do for a smaller automotive alternator. (Use a 60 - 0 - 60 gauge for a bigger 60 amp alternator.) Here's how to read your ammeter's behavior.

For example, your battery should reach its fully charged state within an hour after takeoff. On first starting the engine, the needle will show a high plus

reading and gradually return to a slightly positive indication . . . if the battery, alternator and regulator are all working properly.

On the other hand, if after an hour of flying the ammeter needle still shows a heavy charge (+), your voltage regulator may be set too high, or you may have a bad cell in the battery.

Here's a third condition your ammeter can show you. Immediately after starting the engine, if the ammeter shows a much less than normal charge and begins to taper off even more, it is quite possible that your voltage regulator is set too low and the battery will never become fully charged. It could be, too, that your battery's internal resistance has increased to the point where the battery may be failing.

A second instrument can help you monitor your battery's condition and your electrical system. It is the volt meter.

Some gelled cell batteries, the Globe (now Dynasty) batteries, for example, like a diet of 14.4 to 14.7 volts. On the other hand, my German gelled cell battery, from B&C Specialty Products, thrives on a voltage regulator setting of 13.8 volts. Why the difference?

What seems to be conflicting guidance apparently can be attributed to differing gelled cell battery chemistry and battery temperatures.

A battery exposed to cold conditions requires a higher charging rate than does a battery operating comfortably in a less hostile environment. Is your battery in the engine compartment — (Hot) or is inside the cockpit areas where it is much cooler? Do you live up Nawth or down South?

In any event be guided by the battery charging rate recommendations of your battery's manufacturer.

Lately, many of the batteries being sold by B&C Specialty Products, to aerobatic pilots, are the rela-

133

A typical gelled electrolyte battery. The absence of filler caps for the individual cells is a clue that the battery is sealed and maintenance-free. Note the "L" shaped terminal posts . . . a recognizable feature of all gelled cell aircraft type batteries.

tively new sealed liquid type. They contain a sponge-like material that tends to temporarily absorb the electrolyte whenever the battery is inverted. These batteries have a much lower internal resistance, are lighter, smaller, and pack a lot of power for their size. They too, need a voltage charging rate of 14.6 volts (plus or minus .2).

Now, how do you check your voltage setting? You can verify it with a handheld voltmeter or one you can install in the aircraft. It should be a good one. One that can be read to 0.1 volts.

One nice thing about a voltmeter in the instrument panel — as soon as the master switch is turned on, the gauge will show battery voltage.

With the engine not running, the battery voltage of your fully charged battery will probably be slightly below 12 volts.

Anyway, at a glance you can see if there is enough power in the battery to crank the engine. Of course, in flight the voltmeter should show the voltage output of your alternator.

If your voltage regulator drifts out of calibration and begins to put out higher voltage than originally set, replace the regulator if it is one that cannot be adjusted or you will soon be replacing that battery and every other one that follows it.

The gelled electrolyte battery is a good one. Back it up with a good well adjusted regulator and an over voltage regulator and you will have the power you need when you need it.

USEFUL SOURCE INFORMATION

Aircraft Spruce & Specialty, Box 424, Fullerton, CA 92632, 1-800/824-1930. Gelled cell batteries, regulators, etc.

The AeroElectric Connection, Medicine River Press, Benton Airport, Benton, KS 67017, 316/778-1035. Subscription to "AeroElectric Connection" (Issue 1, $10). Valuable electrical information for all homebuilders.

B&C Specialty Products, Inc., 123 E. 4th St., Newton, KS 67114, 316/283-8000. Gelled cell batteries, linear voltage regulators, etc.

Globe Battery Division, Johnson Controls, Attn: Gel/Cell Marketing, 5757 N. Green Bay Ave., Milwaukee, WI 53201, 414/228-2393. Gel/cell batteries and manual on charging gel/cell batteries/chargers.

Inline inverted 4-cylinder air cooled Hirth 504 A2 engine rated at 105 hp at 2,530 rpm — 75 hp at recommended 2,270 rpm cruise setting — installed in a Klemm 35D a late 30s German designed military trainer.

FUEL SYSTEMS ■ 8 ■

How About an Aluminum Fuel Tank?

Most builders cannot weld aluminum or, to put it more accurately, have never tried to weld aluminum. If so, why should any of them even consider making an aluminum fuel tank? After all, almost anyone can make a serviceable fiberglass or composite fuel tank.

Actually, many a current builder may have no choice when the tank is designed as an integral part of the composite structure in the airplane he is building. However, not everyone is building a plastic airplane and there are many, many homebuilt designs which allow the builder to exercise his individuality and give him the option of making and installing whatever type fuel tank he prefers. I don't consider the choice of fuel tank construction to be a matter of aluminum tanks vs. fiberglass tanks . . . not at all.

Each type of fuel tank construction has its own unique qualities that may make one type better suited to a particular aircraft than the other. Since this article is about metal tanks, let's let them occupy the spotlight.

METAL TANKS, THEIR ATTRIBUTES AND SHORTCOMINGS

A metal fuel tank will almost always be lighter than a fiberglass tank of like capacity. A weight savings of three or more pounds can often be realized in a larger tank.

Aluminum is a clean, stable, easy to work material that always yields predictable results. On the other hand, for those of us who have not had the opportunity to learn how, through expert instruction and plenty of practice, aluminum is difficult to weld. Then, too, most of us don't have the equipment . . .

Aluminum, unlike steel, does not change color as its temperature is increased to the melting point. Furthermore, its lower melting point is reached very suddenly due to its high thermal conductivity. Consequently, the metal will suddenly puddle and collapse leaving a gaping hole much to the unpracticed welder's dismay when he first tries his hand at welding aluminum.

Another characteristic of aluminum is sure to bedevil the inexperienced welder. Compared to steel, it has a much higher rate of expansion. This combined with its high thermal conductivity makes aluminum subject to considerable distortion and warpage during welding, and especially when a continuous seam has to be welded.

An aluminum tank (unlike a fiberglass tank), being

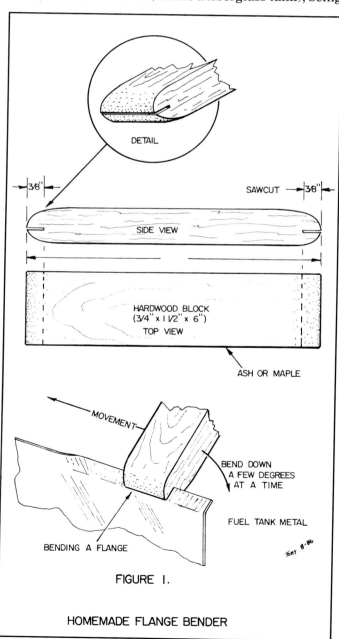

DETAIL

3/8"   SAWCUT   3/8"

SIDE VIEW

HARDWOOD BLOCK
(3/4" x 1 1/2" x 6")
TOP VIEW

ASH OR MAPLE

MOVEMENT

BEND DOWN
A FEW DEGREES
AT A TIME

FUEL TANK METAL

BENDING A FLANGE

Tony 8-86

FIGURE I.

HOMEMADE FLANGE BENDER

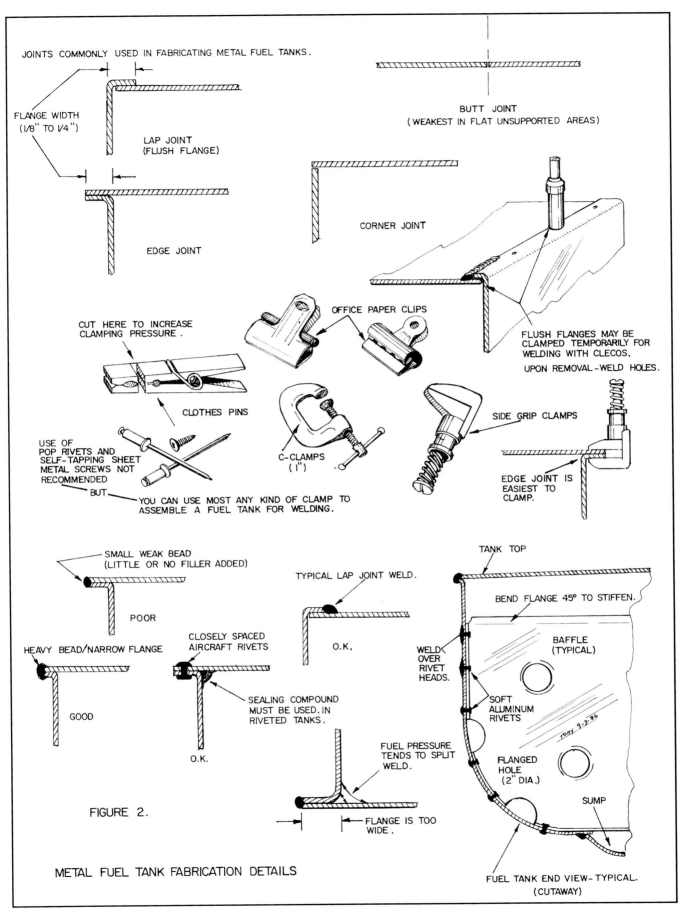

JOINTS COMMONLY USED IN FABRICATING METAL FUEL TANKS.

FLANGE WIDTH
(1/8" TO 1/4")

LAP JOINT
(FLUSH FLANGE)

EDGE JOINT

BUTT JOINT
(WEAKEST IN FLAT UNSUPPORTED AREAS)

CORNER JOINT

FLUSH FLANGES MAY BE
CLAMPED TEMPORARILY FOR
WELDING WITH CLECOS.

UPON REMOVAL - WELD HOLES.

CUT HERE TO INCREASE
CLAMPING PRESSURE.

OFFICE PAPER CLIPS

CLOTHES PINS

USE OF
POP RIVETS AND
SELF-TAPPING SHEET
METAL SCREWS NOT
RECOMMENDED
—— BUT ——

C-CLAMPS
(I")

YOU CAN USE MOST ANY KIND OF CLAMP TO
ASSEMBLE A FUEL TANK FOR WELDING.

SIDE GRIP CLAMPS

EDGE JOINT IS
EASIEST TO
CLAMP.

SMALL WEAK BEAD
(LITTLE OR NO FILLER ADDED)

POOR

HEAVY BEAD/NARROW FLANGE

GOOD

CLOSELY SPACED
AIRCRAFT RIVETS

SEALING COMPOUND
MUST BE USED. IN
RIVETED TANKS.

O.K.

TYPICAL LAP JOINT WELD.

O.K.

FUEL PRESSURE
TENDS TO SPLIT
WELD.

FLANGE IS TOO
WIDE.

TANK TOP

BEND FLANGE 45° TO STIFFEN.

WELD
OVER
RIVET
HEADS.

BAFFLE
(TYPICAL)

SOFT
ALUMINUM
RIVETS

Tony 9-3-86

FLANGED
HOLE
(2" DIA.)

SUMP

FUEL TANK END VIEW- TYPICAL.
(CUTAWAY)

FIGURE 2.

METAL FUEL TANK FABRICATION DETAILS

a good conductor of electricity, can be easily grounded to the aircraft ground during refueling, thereby eliminating the risk of static electricity build-up. (Have the individual doing the refueling attach his grounding cable to your exhaust stack.)

You don't have to be able to weld aluminum to make your own metal tank! And, contrary to what you may believe, it is not difficult, either. It is a relatively simple thing to completely fabricate a tank in your workshop without any special tools except for a homemade flange bending gadget. The external skins can be cut out with tinships, or on a bandsaw, and bent to shape.

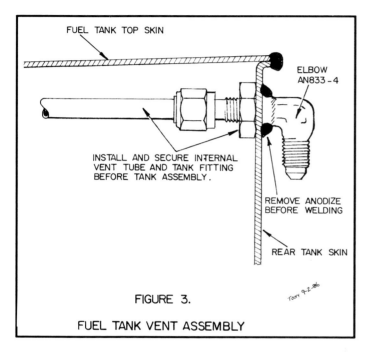

FUEL TANK TOP SKIN

ELBOW
AN833-4

INSTALL AND SECURE INTERNAL VENT TUBE AND TANK FITTING BEFORE TANK ASSEMBLY.

REMOVE ANODIZE BEFORE WELDING

REAR TANK SKIN

FIGURE 3.

FUEL TANK VENT ASSEMBLY

A flange is bent in one of the skins with a homemade flanging tool and then the skins are assembled by clamping the edges together so that you can haul the tank off to be heliarc welded. Of course, I've skipped a few details, but read on.

If you prefer, you can assemble your tank with aircraft rivets so that no welding is necessary. After all, integral wing tanks in metal aircraft are routinely fabricated in this manner, so why not any tank? The riveted seams and rivets must, of course, be sealed with a fuel proof compound.

Note: You may not be aware of it but Aircraft Spruce and Specialty Co. (and others) sells ready made metal tanks for a variety of homebuilt designs. One of these tanks might be suitable for your aircraft.

WHAT MATERIALS TO USE?

Make your tank(s) of .040" or .050" weldable aluminum. If the tank is to be completely riveted and no welding will be required, 2024 T3 grade aluminum alloy sheet may be used. However, 2024 T3, in addition

to being not weldable, is not easily formed except when it is in its annealed (0) condition. Otherwise, use one of the commonly available weldable aluminum alloys like the 1100, 3003, 5052 or 6061 series of aluminum sheet.

I would not use the soft commercial 1100 aluminum as the strength simply is not there. If you use 6061 aluminum, it can be heat treated after welding although this is seldom done by homebuilders. All things considered, the recommended fuel tank material is 5052, either 1/4 or 1/2 hard aluminum. The 5052H32 designation is for the 1/4 hard, and the 5052H34 designation is for the 1/2 hard aluminum. The 5052H32 aluminum is very easy to form and is readily available from homebuilt suppliers.

You can make your baffles of a lighter weight than the .040" or .050" material used for the tank skins. This is because baffles are normally riveted in and do not require welding internally. For this reason, you could also use 2024 T3 if you prefer.

The rivets used for installing baffles must be of the soft (commercial) variety, if their heads must be welded over after installation. Use 1/8" diameter dome head rivets.

Tanks that are to be completely riveted (no welding) may be put together with aircraft rivets (AN470AD-4) closely spaced. A spacing of approximately 5/8" may be suitable in most instances depending on tank design and material thickness employed. A close spacing for rivets is important in obtaining good tight seams that will be leakproof once sealed with a good fuel proof sealing compound.

Standard aluminum weldable flanges may be purchased from your favorite supplier, or you can machine your own from a hunk of weldable aluminum stock. The same holds true for the filler neck and filler cap. Flush caps mated to a solid aluminum mounting ring are quite popular with builders. These filler neck rings may be welded or riveted to the tank providing a flush streamlined installation for the fuel cap.

Each tank must have a sump of some sort, even if it is no more than an exaggerated dent in the bottom of the tank. This depression, or sump, is for the purpose of providing a localized low spot in which water (if present) will settle and be easily drained during a preflight inspection.

TANK DESIGN CONSIDERATIONS

A single large tank is less expensive to make and is more efficient than a couple of smaller tanks. The reason is obvious. Just as much work is required to build one small tank as it takes to build a larger one. Besides, you would have to make and install a filler neck and cap, vent line, sump and finger screen in each tank. In addition, there will be the requirement for installation straps, shut-off valve and duplicate plumbing. A multiple fuel tank installation always increases

The bottom section of the fuel tank being flanged. This jig "B" was dreamed up to provide a "second set of hands". "A" is the homemade flanging tool. It proved to be superior to the storebought wide flanging tool.

Here are the two major components making up this tank. The baffles are fitted and ready to be riveted.

This is going to be the front tank and the area indicated by "A" will be cut out to provide the needed space behind the instrument panel. Note the variety of clamps you can use. The tanks top piece is being fitted. Later the clamps will be used to assemble the complete tank.

The flanged edges have been completed on the tank bottom and the first baffle is being fitted.

The partly welded tank in the weld shop being heliarc welded. Note a couple of clamps indicate areas not yet welded.

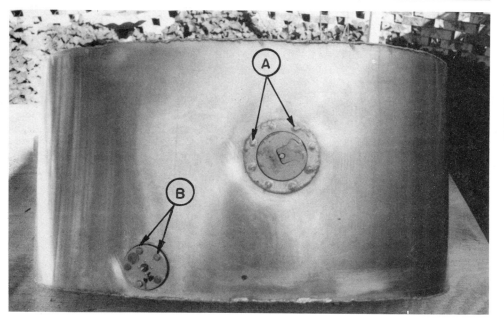

Top view of the tanks shows up the filler cap with welded over rivet heads "A" securing the flange. "B" is the fuel transmitter and bolt heads are not welded. May have to remove it someday.

complexity and introduces fuel management problems. As you may have surmised, the weight increase and added cost will not be welcome either.

Obviously, if your need is for fast long range travel, you'll have to resign yourself to the drawbacks pointed out and go ahead with the building and installation of multiple tanks.

Should you decide on a single tank installation, you will probably experience an overwhelming desire to make that one tank as large as possible. Fine . . . but be careful not to make it so large that it will not fit into its allocated space.

If the tank is to be installed up front in the fuselage, remember that the tank bottom must clear your feet and the rudder pedals, too.

Try to avoid designing an odd shaped tank as that will only complicate its fabrication and perhaps its installation. Simplicity is the goal. Make your tank of as few separate pieces of metal as possible. This will reduce the number of welded seams and simplify assembly. It is possible to make a tank out of two large pieces of aluminum as is evident in the accompanying photos. Even a rectangular tank may be similarly fabricated if a good paper pattern is worked out first.

Of course, in either case there would have to be a separate piece for the sump, and perhaps a couple more pieces for the baffles. Nevertheless, the fewer the number of parts used in fabricating your tank, the less likely that you will have problems with it.

BAFFLES

The primary function of baffles is to minimize the sloshing surge of fuel in the tank during maneuvers. A secondary function is to strengthen the tank by increasing rigidity in the relatively thin metal.

There is an honest difference of opinion over whether baffles are needed in a homebuilt metal tank. I believe a large metal tank should have baffles . . . but what constitutes a large tank? How about 18 gallons? Certainly, the design of a tank can be a factor. Tanks having large flat areas are less likely to "oil can" when strengthened by the presence of baffles. However, you should also be aware that the sloshing fuel can also impose considerable loads on the baffles and rivets securing them. There is the possibility that the soft rivets used could fail and the loosened baffle would then become a liability. The rivet spacing for securing baffles should probably be no further than two inches apart.

FLANGES AND SEAMS

To facilitate the assembly of your tank you will have to form flanges in one or more of the tank skins. These flanges need only be about 1/8" wide for welding. However, a 1/8" flange is difficult to clamp so make yours about 1/4" to 3/8". About 1/16" of that will be melted away in welding. These flanges can be used in different ways as illustrated in Figure 2.

If you don't like the external lip type of welded flange, you might make the flush type. This type of flange poses an assembly problem, however. While the protruding flanges are readily clamped with Cleco side clamps, small C clamps or even large office stationery clamps, the flush type flange has to be clamped some other way. One way could be with pop rivets, but they are tricky to weld over. It could also mean more difficult work for the welder as he would have to weld around each of these assembly rivets. For this reason, the use of pop rivets as an assembly aid is not recommended. Neither is the use of sheet metal screws. Clecos can do a better job, and the small holes drilled for their temporary insertion are easily welded over.

A NOTE OF CAUTION

This is not idle gossip. Many builders have experienced the trauma of cracked seams in welded

The tank is set up to test for leaks. Arrow "A" points to inner tube valve. "B" is a low pressure gage. Tank is pressurized to 2½ psi and soapy water is flowed over all seams and rivet heads to locate leak bubbles, if any.

141

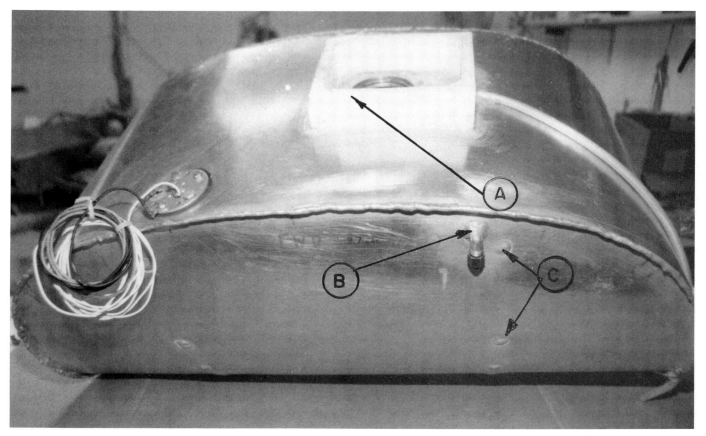

The completed tank. Wires are already connected to the fuel level transmitter unit. Two wires? . . . Wood aircraft. "A" identifies the fuel filler scupper to catch and drain spilled fuel. "B" is the bulkhead AN fitting connecting the vent line. "C" shows the rivet heads already welded over.

aluminum tanks. Some of these were detected at an early stage and others not until the builder felt fuel dripping on his leg, or smelled it in the cockpit, suddenly realizing in a flash of panic that there were hot pulsating exhausts underneath. Terror? You bet!

Every instance of a cracked fuel tank seam (of those I have seen) happened because the seams were improperly welded. The welder had, in most instances, merely melted and fused the flange edges with little or no addition of filler rod. The welds generally looked beautiful with their small uniform beads. But if you have a tank that looks like that you better inspect it closely before every flight, or take it to the welding shop and have some more filler rod added to the welds.

Whoever does the welding on your tank should be aware that it is not a common container. By that I mean he should know that it is a fuel tank which will be subjected to vibration and to internal stresses from surging fuel.

Tell your welder that merely fusing the edges is not acceptable, and that beauty is not your prime concern. You want an extra heavy bead on all your seams. It doesn't matter whether the heavy bead is made on the initial pass or on a second. What is important is that plenty of filler rod be added to the seams.

Standard AN aluminum fittings can be welded into the tank for connecting your tank vent and/or for con-

necting interconnecting tanks. File or sand off the anodized coating before welding.

To my knowledge, I don't know of a single tank welding job that was completed without harboring at least a couple of pin hole leaks. So don't fault your welder if your tank has a few, too. The problem seems to stem from the need to first tack-weld the tank metal every two inches or so to keep it from distorting all out of alignment. Later, when the welder gets to the tack weld, there is a lot of localized metal present that sort of upsets the welding rhythm and the aforementioned pin holes sneak by the welder.

SEALING RIVETED TANKS AND INTEGRAL TANKS

Riveted tanks should be assembled by coating each rib, bulkhead, joint and surface with a light coating of a suitable fuel proof sealing compound. These sealing compounds are not generally available and must be special ordered. A couple are listed below.

Products Research and Chemical Corporation (PRC is a registered trademark of Monsanto Company) has a product long used by at least one of the major aircraft manufacturers of military aircraft, and by a good number of BD-4 builders. It is PR-1422 Class B, a filleting compound developed specifically for sealing integral fuel tanks. A related product, PRC 1005-L, is applied as a protective coating over synthetic rubber sealants such as the PR-1422. It is a thin substance and is apparently used in a manner not unlike other sloshing compounds.

My somewhat dated files show the address for the PRC products to be Products Research Corporation, P.O. Box 1800, Glendale, CA 91209 (213/240-2060).

Another company, Essex Chemical Corporation, Coast Pro-Seal Division, 19451 Susana Rd., Compton, CA 90221 also manufactures a large variety of sealants such as Pro-Seal 707 and EP-711 (P.S. 890B-2). EP 711 is currently being used by builders of RV aircraft to seal the integral wing tanks. RV builders can order this sealant through Van's Aircraft, P.O. Box 160, North Plains, OR 97133 or from Packaging Systems, Inc., 1517 Flower St., Glendale, CA 91201 (213/246-5568).

The shelf life of most fuel tank sealants is rather short — approximately six months at room temperature. This means that you shouldn't order the sealant unless you can use it within that time frame.

It is essential that the metal tank surfaces to be coated with the sealant be squeaky clean. Clean the surfaces with methyl ethyl ketone (MEK) or Naptha, or whatever cleaner is stipulated in the instructions. Be absolutely certain that you do not touch the cleaned surfaces with your bare hands as the body oils will ruin your seal at each point of contact.

Applying the sealant is a very messy operation but a critical one for which there are no short cuts. After the rivets have been upset, run a 1/8" bead or fillet of sealant along every rib, seam, corner, joint and rivet. Do a thorough job of it and you won't be bothered with fuel seepage or leaks. Sealant is most effectively applied on the pressure side of the tank surfaces . . . that is, on the inside of the tank and not the outside.

What about a sloshing compound? Some say use it and others are a bit leary about using it in view of the additives oil companies are putting in auto gas. If you intend to use auto gas you might be wise in not sloshing your tank. The presence of methanol (alcohol) can soften and loosen the sloshing compound to the point where it could deteriorate sufficiently to clog your fuel system. The ultimate consequence? Engine failure due to fuel starvation. If your tank has been sloshed, the advice is to avoid the use of any fuel with additives unless you know that the additive doesn't include methanol or some equally incompatible substance. Check the inside of your tank(s) regularly if they are sloshed.

TESTING THE TANK FOR LEAKS

There is an easy way to do this. Seal all tank openings and attach a low pressure gage to the tank sump. Add about 1 or 2 psi of air pressure . . . never more than 3 psi! Coat the external surfaces of the tank with soapy water and brush over all the seams with the soap suds. Examine every square inch carefully looking for air bubbles which indicate the presence of a pin hole leak. Repeat the process a couple of times until you have reassured yourself that you have found all the leak sources or have been unable to detect any.

If your welded tank has a pin hole leak, mark around the area with a black felt pen and take your tank back to the welder for corrective action.

On getting the tank back, check it for leaks again. Don't assume it will be O.K. just because you expect it to be. Be absolutely sure that tank doesn't leak! It takes a tremendous effort to remove and reinstall a fuel tank after you get the airplane flying. In some instances you may have to remove the entire instrument panel and most of the electrical wiring to get it out.

Building a metal tank is a satisfying experience for anyone, but even more so for the builder who feels that his aluminum tank will free him of that nagging concern that he might someday have to use fuel that could adversely affect a fiberglass tank.

USEFUL FUEL TANK REFERENCES

SPORT AVIATION —
"The Fuel Management Problem," Oct. 1979
"Fuel Tanks," Aug., Sept., Oct., Nov., Dec. 1982

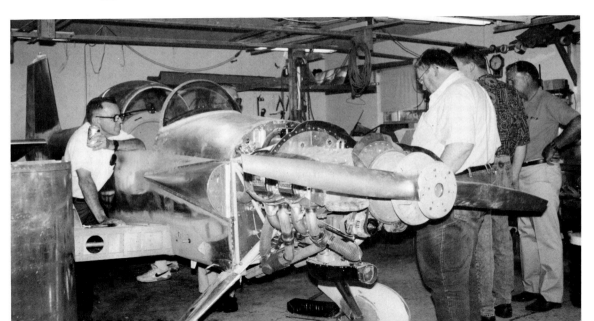

Expert advice without even asking!

143

The Basic Fuel Pump System

A gravity flow fuel system will not work in many aircraft designs — especially in most low wing types. As you know, a fuel pump system must be used whenever the fuel tanks cannot be installed high enough above the level of the carburetor to take advantage of gravity and the simple, efficient, gravity flow system.

Does that infer, then, that a fuel pump system is more complex than a gravity flow system? Yes, indeed, unfortunately.

We know that man's best efforts can never equal nature's simplicity and efficiency. Therefore, it's not surprising that the seemingly simple solution of adding a fuel pump only partially copes with the problem of delivering fuel to an engine without the help of gravity. Gravity never fails but fuel pumps do. So, to protect yourself from that eventuality, you will have to add a back-up pump of some sort.

Now you have two pumps — but how do you know how well they are working? That's right, you must also install a fuel pressure gauge, or a fuel flow meter (which in reality is nothing more than a fuel pressure gauge) to give you that information.

There you have it — just a hint of the added complexity that sets a basic fuel pump system apart from a gravity flow fuel system.

THE BASIC FUEL SYSTEM COMPONENTS

In all respects, the fuel pump system is quite similar to the gravity flow system. Both systems begin at the fuel tanks.

Fuel delivery starts as the fuel passes through a finger screen protected outlet in the bottom of the fuel tank. From the tank, the fuel flows through an aluminum line (at least 3/8" in diameter) to a conveniently located fuel selector valve in the cockpit.

After passing through that tank selector valve, the fuel heads for the main filter, better known as the "gascolator". The gascolator is generally located on the firewall and should be the lowest component in the fuel system. It is always fitted with a quick drain valve so that the entire fuel system can be drained at that point. The gascolator also provides a convenient means for draining some fuel to check for the presence of water during your preflight inspection. The quick drain

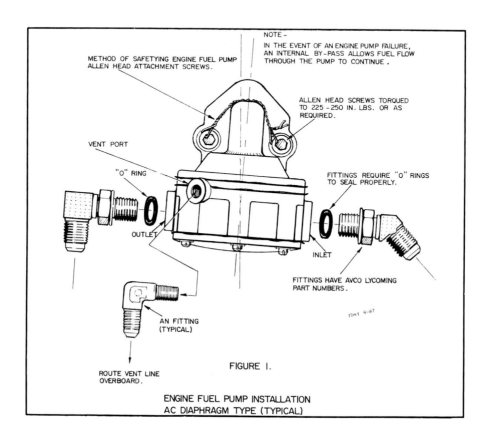

NOTE -
IN THE EVENT OF AN ENGINE PUMP FAILURE, AN INTERNAL BY-PASS ALLOWS FUEL FLOW THROUGH THE PUMP TO CONTINUE.

METHOD OF SAFETYING ENGINE FUEL PUMP ALLEN HEAD ATTACHMENT SCREWS.

ALLEN HEAD SCREWS TORQUED TO 225 - 250 IN. LBS. OR AS REQUIRED.

VENT PORT

"O" RING

FITTINGS REQUIRE "O" RINGS TO SEAL PROPERLY.

OUTLET

INLET

FITTINGS HAVE AVCO LYCOMING PART NUMBERS.

TONY 4-87

AN FITTING (TYPICAL)

ROUTE VENT LINE OVERBOARD.

FIGURE I.

ENGINE FUEL PUMP INSTALLATION
AC DIAPHRAGM TYPE (TYPICAL)

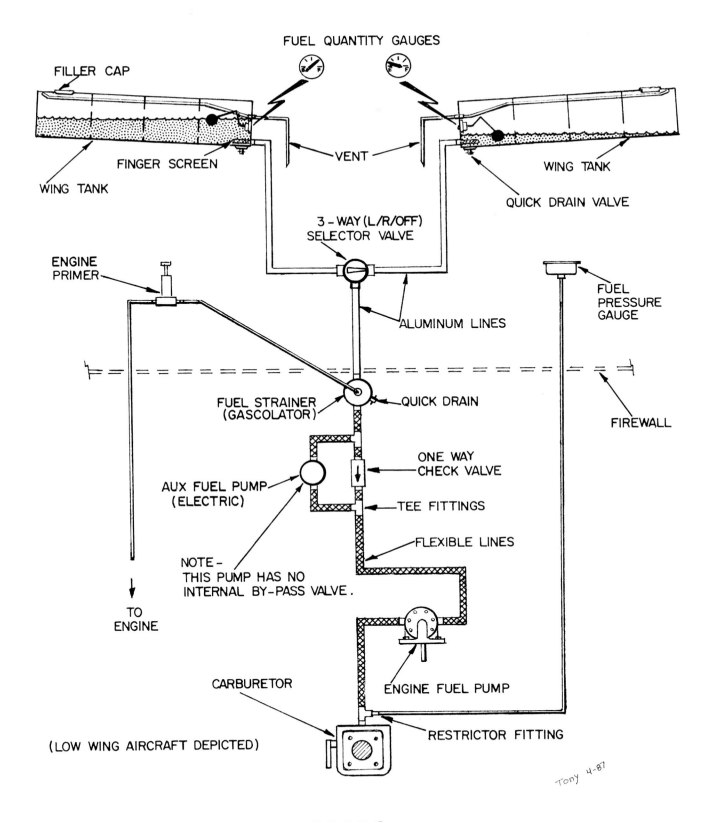

FUEL QUANTITY GAUGES

FILLER CAP

FINGER SCREEN

WING TANK

VENT

WING TANK

QUICK DRAIN VALVE

3-WAY (L/R/OFF) SELECTOR VALVE

ENGINE PRIMER

ALUMINUM LINES

FUEL PRESSURE GAUGE

FUEL STRAINER (GASCOLATOR)

QUICK DRAIN

FIREWALL

ONE WAY CHECK VALVE

AUX FUEL PUMP (ELECTRIC)

TEE FITTINGS

FLEXIBLE LINES

NOTE - THIS PUMP HAS NO INTERNAL BY-PASS VALVE.

TO ENGINE

ENGINE FUEL PUMP

CARBURETOR

(LOW WING AIRCRAFT DEPICTED)

RESTRICTOR FITTING

Tony 4-87

FIGURE 2.

FUEL PUMP SYSTEM SCHEMATIC

Both of these are high pressure auxiliary fuel pumps intended for installation in a fuel injected engine. The pump on the left has no internal by-pass valve and must be installed in parallel with the engine driven pump. The pump on the right has an internal by-pass and can be installed in series with the engine driven fuel pump. Which would you use?

should be easily accessible without have to remove any cowling or covers.

Incidentally, has it ever occurred to you that when you drain fuel out of the gascolator to check for water, you are only checking the tank that the selector is set on? If you want to check any other tank, you must change the selector setting and drain some more fuel. Right?

After the filtered fuel passes through the gascolator, it enters, or bypasses, a back-up pump. This unit is usually an electric pump but could also be a hand-operated wobble pump.

Finally, the fuel reaches the heart of the fuel pump system — the engine driven pump. This mechanical engine driven pump is bolted directly to an accessory pad on the engine crankcase from whence it delivers the fuel under pressure to the fuel injector or carburetor.

NOTE: It is important to know that, although your engine driven pump is the primary source of fuel pressure, a backup auxiliary fuel pump is a mandatory installation for aircraft manufactured under an Approved Type Certificate. Certainly, your own amateur-built aircraft should be likewise equipped.

Since these fuel pumps must provide sufficient pressure to move the fuel from the tank(s) to the carburetor or fuel injector, it is obvious that you should have some way of knowing that the required pressure is being produced. As already pointed out, this little matter is taken care of with the installation of a fuel pressure gauge.

The added complexity of the fuel pump system, compared to the gravity flow system, will become more apparent to you after you start your installation. Let's see what is involved.

THE FUEL PRESSURE GAUGE INSTALLATION

The fuel pressure gauge you install must be calib-

rated to accommodate the fuel pressure range for your system. For example, a fuel injector operates with a normal fuel pressure of approximately 24 psi while a pressure type carburetor will not require more than 15 psi. A conventional float type carburetor requires even less pressure to operate efficiently . . . about 5 psi. So you see, you should install a gauge that will read high enough for your installation. On the other hand, a fuel pressure gauge capable of registering a much higher pressure than that needed for your installation may not be as accurate as a gauge calibrated for a lesser fuel pressure range.

A rare view of an AC diaphragm engine driven fuel pump uncluttered by the usual hoses, controls, and wires that virtually hide the pump from view. Note its general location on a Lycoming O-320 engine.

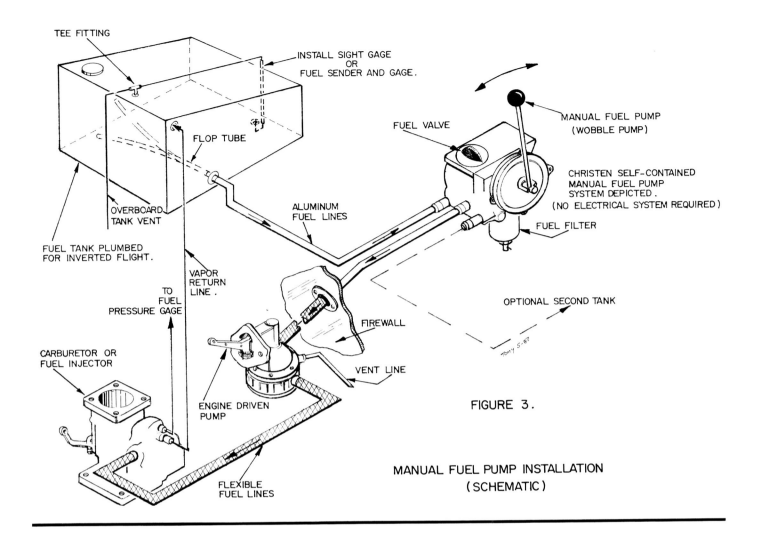

TEE FITTING

INSTALL SIGHT GAGE
OR
FUEL SENDER AND GAGE.

FUEL VALVE

MANUAL FUEL PUMP
(WOBBLE PUMP)

CHRISTEN SELF-CONTAINED
MANUAL FUEL PUMP
SYSTEM DEPICTED.
(NO ELECTRICAL SYSTEM REQUIRED)

FLOP TUBE

FUEL FILTER

ALUMINUM
FUEL LINES

OVERBOARD
TANK VENT

FUEL TANK PLUMBED
FOR INVERTED FLIGHT.

VAPOR
RETURN
LINE.

TO
FUEL
PRESSURE GAGE

OPTIONAL SECOND TANK

FIREWALL

CARBURETOR OR
FUEL INJECTOR

VENT LINE

FIGURE 3.

ENGINE DRIVEN
PUMP

FLEXIBLE
FUEL LINES

MANUAL FUEL PUMP INSTALLATION
(SCHEMATIC)

There is one more consideration. The typical individual fuel pressure gauge will be either 2-1/4" or 2-1/16" (automotive type) in diameter. Better check your gauge size before cutting that instrument panel hole. Fuel pressure gauges are also available as part of an "instrument cluster". These are quite popular and are used by most aircraft manufacturers. The choice is yours.

Installing a fuel pressure gauge is fairly simple. After the gauge is mounted in the instrument panel, or in some other more convenient location if need be, the instrument is connected to the carburetor or fuel injector using standard AN fittings. Since the line will be full of raw fuel all the way from the carburetor to the cockpit panel, it would seem prudent to use tubing of a smaller diameter than that used for your main fuel supply lines. After all, only pressure is being measured, and that has nothing to do with the flow or fuel to the engine. A 1/8" or a 3/16" aluminum line should, therefore, suffice. Connect the fuel pressure line, using a restrictor type fitting, to the port in your fuel injector or carburetor housing provided for that purpose.

While you would normally use an aluminum line

from the fuel pressure gauge to the firewall bulkhead fitting, the fuel pressure line inside the engine compartment (from the firewall to the fuel injector or carburetor) should be a flexible aircraft hose fabricated with standard metal fittings) see Figures 2, 3 and 4).

In my opinion, plastic hoses and slip-on fittings secured with clamps or wire twists, have no place in the primary fuel or oil system — especially, inside the engine compartment.

YOUR ENGINE DRIVEN FUEL PUMP

During all normal engine operations, the engine driven (mechanical) fuel pump automatically delivers the fuel at the proper pressure directly to the nearby fuel injector, or carburetor as the case may be.

The well known AC diaphragm-type aircraft fuel pump is considered to be the industry standard engine pump for most small aircraft engines. It is a self-priming type pump with specially developed diaphragms that seem to be unaffected by the various exotic chemical properties making up fuels these days (see Figure 1).

Not many moons ago, the AC folks decided to cancel production of their fuel pump repair kits because too many fuel pumps were being improperly repaired. They figured that the cost difference between the repair of an old pump and the installment of a new one was not worth the problems being encountered. So, forget about overhauling your old AC type engine driven fuel pump. Repair kits are no longer available.

There is a bit more on the AC engine pump thing. The later model pumps have been given new Lycoming and AC numbers that supersede the old style pump numbers . . . but that's not all.

When replacing a failed old pump with a new style one, I found that my old inlet and outlet port fittings did not fit the new pump. What a surprise to learn that a 30 minute installation would drag out into a week long search for the correct fittings.

In the end, to make the change I had the unwelcome choice of purchasing special Weatherhead — or Lycoming engine pump fittings — complete with "O" rings (see Figure 1).

When the correct engine driven fuel pump is installed, it will discharge (pump) more fuel than your engine needs . . . actually the pump should be capable of providing a minimum fuel flow of 125% of that required for maximum take-off power. This excess capacity will not be a problem in the operation of your engine as an internal relief valve — factory adjusted to deliver the fuel at the correct pressure for a particular carburetor or fuel injector installation — prevents the development of excessive fuel pressure at the fuel inlet.

I know of an instance where the builder was unable to maintain cruise engine power unless his electric boost pump was turned on and running. A lot of smart folks were stumped by this problem until someone found the obvious — the engine driven pump was the wrong type, and not large enough to feed that fuel injected engine without the help of an auxiliary pump.

Be sure when you do buy a new pump that it has the correct part number for your engine. Also, check to see what type fittings you will need. These are generally hard to find.

Engine driven fuel pumps have achieved a remarkable reliability record, but they do fail. Most commonly, the diaphragm ruptures and fuel comes squirting out of the drain line. Such a failure, if it does happen, is, I believe, most often the result of age and not due to a material deficiency.

If yours happens to be a well used engine whose Engine Log makes no mention of the engine driven fuel pump, consider the fuel pump to be operating on borrowed time and overdue for replacement.

Just keep this in mind. A failed engine driven fuel pump can create a serious fire hazard if the diaphragm ruptures and if the vent has not been connected to a line routed away from the hot exhaust pipes to a safe overboard location. Furthermore, the engine won't run any more . . . not without the help of a back-up fuel pump.

Such an auxiliary pump can keep your engine running even with a failed engine driven pump. This is

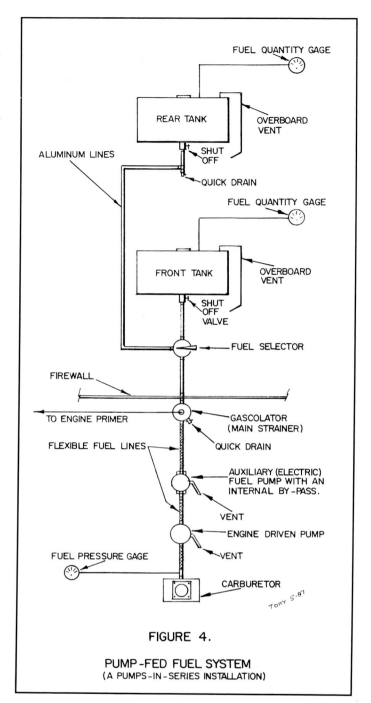

FIGURE 4.

PUMP-FED FUEL SYSTEM
(A PUMPS-IN-SERIES INSTALLATION)

possible because the AC type engine driven fuel pumps (and the Thompson and the Romec pumps as well) have an internal bypass valve that allows the fuel to flow through the engine driven pump even after it has failed. Without this provision, the installation and use of a back up pump would be greatly complicated.

BACK-UP PUMP OPTIONS

A back-up by any other name may be an auxiliary pump, boost pump, electric pump or even a wobble pump. They all serve the same purpose — that of helping the engine driven pump or, in extreme cases, taking over its function completely.

The address: Sun Magic International, P.O. Box 634681, Margate, Florida 33063-7629.

Cleaning and Degreasing Materials — Add to your need list a couple of "SCOTCH BRITE" pads, and a plentiful supply of solvents. (Methyl Ethyl Ketone MEK, Toluene, Acetone, Lacquer Thinner, etc.). Use one of the solvents recommended for the type sealant you will be using. When no particular solvent is recommended, I use MEK. Also handy is a good supply of cheese cloth or clean rags. Ban all paper towels from your work area while working with tank sealants. The paper towels will shred and stick to your gloves, tools, work, everything and, in general, will make one of those legendary "tar and feather" orgies look like a white gloves affair by comparison.

Mixing and Application Tools — Most fuel tank sealants are rather thick and require the use of a stout spatula for mixing and spreading the sealant. You might get by using popsicle sticks or tongue depressors, but I find that a couple of hand made aluminum spatulas are better. They won't break and are easier to clean and reuse. Make the metal strips about 1/2" wide and approximately 6" long. Use 2024 T3 aluminum and very slightly round all edges. A couple of aluminum strips with rounded ends will be useful later for forming fillets with the sealant.

Don't use the same spatula to dish out the accelerator and the base compound . . . at least not before cleaning it. If you aren't careful you will contaminate your supply and set off the activation process in both containers.

Other Needs — A rivet gun and bucking bar, naturally. But, also, plenty of Clecos. I would suggest you keep a coffee can, half full of solvent, handy into which you can plunk the contaminated Clecos as you remove them during the riveting process. You can do this without slowing down your work. Later, at a more convenient time, you can finish cleaning the Clecos.

Note: If you forget to clean your Clecos before the sealant cures, or epoxy, or anything else hardens on them, scorch the tips of the Clecos with a bunsen torch. Do not heat the metal too much or it will lose its temper (chuckle). Work the Cleco with Cleco pliers and brush off the residue with a wire brush or a card file. When cleaning solvents fail, try the scorch method . . . it always works.

And last but not the least important is a scale capable of weighing small amounts. I use a small Japanese household scale that is calibrated in grams.

Measure the sealant by weight not by volume because it is so sticky and the accelerator portion is so small that measuring its volume would require very careful formulation.

ABOUT FUEL TANK SEALANTS

Fuel tank sealants have been around a long time and are used extensively in military and commercial aircraft for sealing fuel cells, pressurized compartments, doors and for a variety of purposes. However, it was not until the highly exploited tiny BD-5 came along that many homebuilders first learned about a remarkable sealant called "PRO-SEAL," and about riveted integral fuel tanks in general.

The fuel tank sealants most used are typically two-part, polysulfide, liquid polymer compounds which cure at room temperatures to a resilient rubber-like substance having excellent adhesion qualities. These sealants adhere tenaciously to aluminum, magnesium, titanium, steel and a variety of other materials. They also remain outstandingly resistant to aviation gasoline, jet fuel, petroleum based oils, and hydraulic fluids — and still remain effective during temperature extremes of minus 65 degrees F. to plus 275 degrees F. (that's probably well within the range of temperatures maintained in your workshop).

Pre-measured tank sealants may be obtained in two-part cartridges for use with an extrusion gun or for hand extrusion. These simplify the mixing and application of the sealant. However, the cartridge kits are more expensive and can be wasteful for smaller jobs as the sealant, once mixed, must be used within the specified minimum application life . . . this could be as little as 1/2 hour, depending upon the sealant used.

Sealants are formulated for brush application or for filleting. For example, PRC-1422 Class B (manufactured by Products Research and Chemical Corp.) is a non-brushable filleting compound type of sealant with the consistency of thick paste. PRC-1422 Class A is a thin brushable sealant. The number following the PRC number is the working life of the sealant. That is, PRC-1422 B1/2 has a minimum application life of 1/2 hour while PRC-1422 B4 would have a working life of about 4 hours. I think that either the PRC-1422 A2 or B2 is just about right for us with their 2 hour minimum application life. If you intend to use only one type of sealant, you might prefer to use the brushable type as it is easier to apply to the facing surfaces of the ribs and skins, and still get a fairly respectable fillet build-up where needed. It will not do as good a job where gaps and voids must be sealed over. Still, although thinner than the PRC-1422 B, the PRC-1422 A sealant, once applied to rivet heads or fasteners, will not drip or flow from vertical surfaces either.

PREPARING THE TANK SURFACES

The areas of the ribs and skins that will be in contact with each other (faying surfaces) can be lightly scuffed with SCOTCH BRITE pads and cleaned thoroughly with an oil-free solvent to dissolve any surface oil or wax. (Do not use those "bargain priced" reclaimed solvents for this purpose.)

The recommended cleaning procedure is to wash one small area at a time, drying it with a clean cloth before the solvent evaporates. This procedure will pre-

In the foreground you can see one of the two RV-4's wing tanks being assembled as an integral portion of the basic wing structure. The unique feature of the design is that the wing tanks can be removed for final sealing and riveting.

The tank has been removed from the wing jig for final assembly. The end ribs have already been sealed and riveted using a rivet squeezer. Note the "No No" markings on the embossed rings . . . didn't want to goof by cutting them out as lightening holes. That simple stand is an excellent aid for single handed riveting.

This is an inboard view of both tanks showing the access plates for the fuel pick-up and the fuel sender units. Visible, too, are the vent outlets (B).

154

The internal stiffeners (A) and the sump drain plug (B) on the bottom skins have already been sealed and riveted. Note that the sealant was squeezed out at each rivet location. The excess sealant must be removed from the skin before it cures and hardens.

vent the resettling of the loosened surface wax or oil. Another precaution . . . resist wetting your cleaning cloth by holding it to the solvent can opening and tilting the can to wet it. Do that a few times and you will have contaminated the entire contents with that "dirty" cleaning rag.

I know it is hard to remember, and awkward to do, but always pour the solvent onto the cleaning rag. And, along the same vein, do not use commercial cleaning rags or any cloths that might have wax, oil or soap residue in them.

After the metal surfaces have been cleaned, take care that you do not handle them with your bare hands.

SEALANT APPLICATION

Apply the sealant with a stiff short bristled brush or with one of the aluminum spatulas described earlier. A thin, even coating, approximately 1/32" thick, should be applied to each of the faying surfaces. This double coating will almost guarantee that the fuel will not "wick" along any of the seams and exit at some distance from the place (rivet, fastener or gap) where the leak originated. Do not apply thick coatings. In applications like wing tanks, a thick sealant layer makes riveting more difficult and may even alter the profile fit of the

wing tank to the wing, causing a slight mismatch.

Join the two parts and install Clecos in every other rivet hole following the basic sequence detailed in Figure 2.

Later, after all the rivets have been bucked, go back and coat each rivet and fastener with the sealant so that none of the rivet metal shows. Using a small stiff brush, coat all the rivets, nuts and bolts with sealant by working the brush in a circular action to deposit an even coating of sealant over each fastener.

After this has been done use your spatula or extrusion gun with a 1/8" or slightly larger nozzle opening to form generous fillets along the edges of all seams and in all corners. Pack the sealant firmly in place being careful to work out air pockets.

Next, and this is very important, use a small inspection mirror to examine behind each rivet and fastener to see that it is completely coated with sealant. Any leak which may develop can only originate at a poorly sealed rivet, fastener or gap. See Figure 1 for examples of potential leak sources. The aluminum tank skin itself cannot leak — so why coat the entire inside of the tank? It only adds weight. Put the sealant where it is needed only, otherwise you will use much more sealant than expected. You should be able to seal two 15 gallon

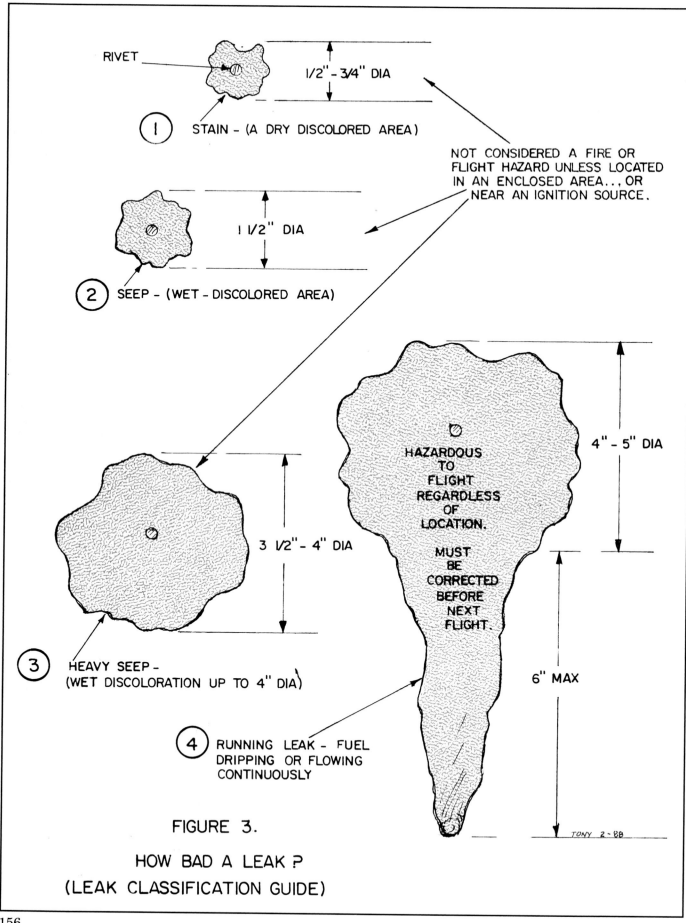

RIVET

1/2" – 3/4" DIA

① STAIN – (A DRY DISCOLORED AREA)

NOT CONSIDERED A FIRE OR
FLIGHT HAZARD UNLESS LOCATED
IN AN ENCLOSED AREA.., OR
NEAR AN IGNITION SOURCE.

1 1/2" DIA

② SEEP – (WET – DISCOLORED AREA)

3 1/2" – 4" DIA

③ HEAVY SEEP –
(WET DISCOLORATION UP TO 4" DIA)

4" – 5" DIA

HAZARDOUS
TO
FLIGHT
REGARDLESS
OF
LOCATION.

MUST
BE
CORRECTED
BEFORE
NEXT
FLIGHT.

6" MAX

④ RUNNING LEAK – FUEL
DRIPPING OR FLOWING
CONTINUOUSLY

TONY 2-88

FIGURE 3.

HOW BAD A LEAK ?

(LEAK CLASSIFICATION GUIDE)

Here is the extent of the laboratory equipment used. A small Japanese household scale calibrated in grams, a small plastic container and two spatulas. One for dishing out the sealing compound and the other for the accelerator. Only small 100 gram batches were mixed at one time.

wing tanks with one quart of sealant.

NOTE: You must remember to protect your vent line opening to keep it from becoming blocked with sealant. Also, take special care that the finger screen (fuel pick up), the fuel sender float and mechanism, and the quick drain outlet don't become "glued up" with sealant, and inoperative. It is just as important to remember to remove the protective covers from the vents, finger screens, and drains after the sealing and riveting is completed — but before the tank is closed.

Just one more time. Go back and examine the sealant areas to see that you have obtained a completely bubble-free continuous coating of sealant. Sometimes an occasional bubble will surface an hour or so after you have completed your work. Repair such spots by adding a little dab of sealant.

GUARDING AGAINST PIN LEAKS

Sometimes, no matter how thoroughly you think your sealing job has been, a pesky pin hole leak will show up when you test the tanks. Many builders, to guard against this possibility, will apply a protective coating over the sealant.

The manufacturer of the popular PRC 1422 sealant (Products Research and Chemical Corp.) recommends the appolication of a brush coating of PR-1005L if a topcoating is desired.

Many builders prefer to flush their tanks with a sloshing compound to help insure that all pin holes are sealed. Just as effective a way would be to simply brush the sloshing compound over all the fasteners and joints before sealing the tank. If you prefer the fill and slosh method be careful that you don't plug up your vent line, fuel pick up, fuel sender and sump drain with the stuff. At least three brush coats (or poured sloshings) is recommended. Allow sufficient time between treatments for the sloshing compound to dry.

If you intend to use automotive fuel with the risk that sometimes, you might unknowingly get fuel with aromatic additives, you might be interested in sloshing your tanks with the relatively new sloshing compounds put out by Randolph Products especially for this purpose. I have not seen any test results nor have I had any input from builders regarding its effectiveness so all I can report is that the new sloshing compound is white in color.

Now, if you are positive that your tank is completely sealed internally, you can, with confidence, install the access plates and covers — after coating them and the fasteners with sealant . . . otherwise simply install them temporarily without sealant until after the leak test.

CHECKING THE TANKS FOR LEAKS

A safe way to check for leaks is with air pressure and soapy water.

Some builders check their tanks by putting fuel or water in them. I don't feel comfortable with either method. The preferred method, I believe, is to check for leaks with air pressure and soapy water. The method is simple to use and is quite effective. There is still another method . . . one I like best, now. It is the one where an ordinary balloon is fitted to any tank inlet or outlet. then, the tank is pressurized until the balloon expands to about 10". The air pressure is shut off and, if the next day the balloon is still inflated — you have a tank that doesn't leak. To pressurize the tank use an air hose, and a bicycle valve stem connected to one of the tank outlets.

First, install the non-vented filler cap or tape over the opening to seal it. Near the bottom of the tank you will have a fuel outlet fitting, a vent line connection and a drain plug. You can use any two of these openings for checking the tank.

You can see how messy the sealant process can become from the appearance of the bench and the stand. Those white areas along the tank rib edges are the new automotive fuel resistant Sloshing Compound put out by Randolph. The small bar clamps are used to insure a tight even seam along the aft fuel tank bulkhead while the sealant is curing.

Next, connect a low pressure gage to one of the openings. It should be capable of indicating as little as 2 or 3 psi.

Then press the end of an air nozzle to the vent line outlet and fill the tank with air until the pressure on the gage reads 2 psi . . . certainly no more than 2-1/2 psi or the tank could puff up ominously and perhaps become permanently distorted. When the 2 psi pressure is reached, take the air nozzle away from the opening and slip a previously prepared wood plug into the fitting or otherwise cap it. (Naturally, if you did not use the sump drain outlet for checking the tank, it should be sealed by installing a quick drain valve or taping it over.)

To check the tank for leaks, brush soapy water over all the rows of rivets, along the tank ends, around the filler neck, drain sump and around the fuel transmitter access plate.

Oh yes, a leak, if there is one, will most probably show up as perky little bubbles at some rivet location. Pin hole leaks are sealed from the inside with additional sealant applied at their source. Be sure to let out the air, wipe the tank dry and clean the area with MEK before applying more sealant. That should do it. Now you can reinstall the access plates permanently.

SUPPLY SOURCES FOR FUEL TANK SEALANTS

Source for all types of sealants/cartridges: Products Research and Chemical Corp., Marketing Services Dept., 5430 San Fernando Rd., PO Box 1800, Glendale, CA 91209, phone 818/240-2060.

Source for two part sealant cartridges: Sealpak Co., Inc., 2614 S. Hoover, Wichita, KS 67215, phone 316/942-6211.

Fuel Pump System Notes

(Essentials)

Here they are . . . and not necessarily in the order of their importance:

1. The fuel tank(s)
2. Fuel tank vent(s)
3. Finger screen
4. Gascolator
5. Fuel quantity indicator
6. Fuel selector valve
7. Suitable fuel lines and fittings
8. Primer
9. Fuel tank tests
10. The fuel flow test

These are the bare minimum needs for a safe and efficient fuel pump type system installation for your homebuilt. However, incorporating all these features in fabricating your fuel system will not automatically ensure its reliability . . . not unless each is properly fabricated, plumbed (installed), and functioning.

The discussion that follows can be helpful in developing the fuel system for your own project. If nothing more, you can use it as a comparative checklist to ensure that you have not overlooked anything important.

THE FUEL TANK(S)

It seems that most high performance composite kits

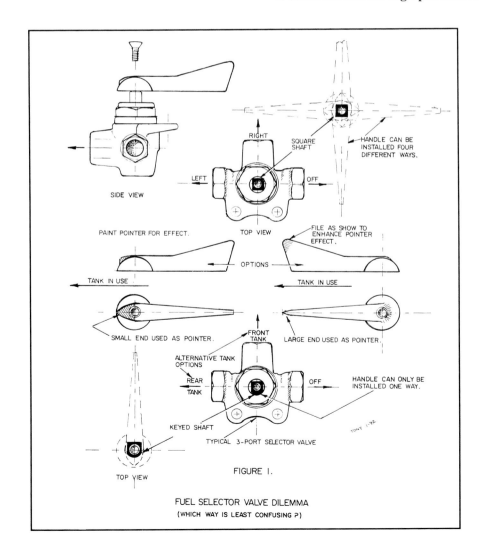

SIDE VIEW

PAINT POINTER FOR EFFECT.

RIGHT

SQUARE SHAFT

HANDLE CAN BE INSTALLED FOUR DIFFERENT WAYS.

LEFT

OFF

TOP VIEW

FILE AS SHOW TO ENHANCE POINTER EFFECT.

OPTIONS

TANK IN USE

TANK IN USE

SMALL END USED AS POINTER.

LARGE END USED AS POINTER.

FRONT TANK

ALTERNATIVE TANK OPTIONS

REAR TANK

OFF

HANDLE CAN ONLY BE INSTALLED ONE WAY.

KEYED SHAFT

TYPICAL 3-PORT SELECTOR VALVE

TONY 1-92

TOP VIEW

FIGURE I.

FUEL SELECTOR VALVE DILEMMA
(WHICH WAY IS LEAST CONFUSING ?)

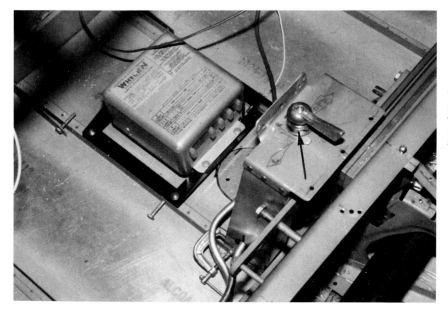

Which way is OFF? Before you install the fuel selector valve — blow into each port and label the tank serviced in each position. Beware if the valve stem is square and the handle can be installed in any of 4 positions . . . See Figure 1.

feature fiberglass fuel tanks built into the wings. Often a small fiberglass header tank is also built into the fuselage.

On the other hand, other less expensive lightplane kits featuring mixed construction usually offer optional ready-made fuselage or wing tanks fabricated of fiberglass.

In contrast, the projects built from plans are, in many instances, older designs and the fuel tank's depicted are shown to be made of aluminum.

Fiberglass Tank — If your tanks are to be fabricated of fiberglass, be absolutely sure that the resin (epoxy, polyester or vinylester) you intend to use is one that will not be adversely affected by aviation fuel or auto gas.

Many resins, especially epoxy resins, are not compatible with fuel.

I know from personal experience, and have learned from the experiences of others, that some resins, if used, may in time result in delaminated seams, soft spots and fuel tank leaks. To be absolutely sure this won't happen to you, you should personally check the resin's compatibility with the fuel you will be using. Make up a few test samples early in the project and store them submerged in fuel for at least a few months.

The vinylester resin (used with the Glasair kit) seems to be quite impervious to 100LL aviation fuel . . . as are some polyester and epoxy resins. However, all these may not fair as well when exposed to auto gas containing alcohol type additives.

I only have one recommendation to make. Avoid using auto fuels containing methanol, or any other exotic aromatic additives, as they will in time ruin most any installed fiberglass tank, plastic fuel line, or car-

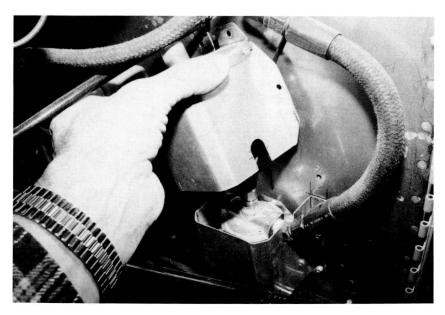

This cooling shroud provides easy access to the gascolator. The cool air is ducted from the rear baffle and into the top of the metal shroud to minimize vapor lock potential.

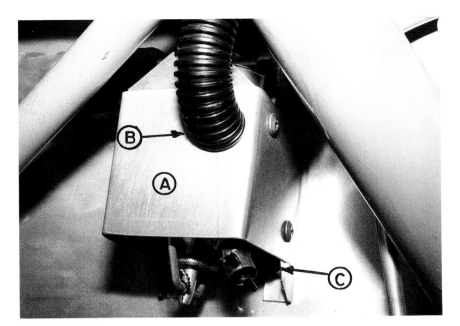

This gascolator is protected from the engine heat with a simple aluminum cover (A) into which cool air from the rear engine baffle is fed through the ducting (B). The quick-drain valve (C) is more useful if it can be reached from outside without having to remove the cowling.

grees F.

Well, so much for the basic fuel system installation.

Now, what about the various fuel system problems we hear about so often?

FUEL STARVATION

Fuel starvation, at the very least, means a forced landing or, worse, a crash landing which may or may not be fatal. There are a number of causes for this problem. The most mortifying being that the pilot simply allows the engine to run out of fuel.

Why in the world would any pilot allow such a thing to happen? Well, it is never intentional. And seldom is it due to mechanical failure.

So, who or what is to blame? Believe it or not, sometimes the fuel system installation or the design of the individual component parts may trick the pilot into jumping to the wrong conclusion or taking the wrong corrective action.

Here are the most frequently cited causes for fuel starvation:

1. Taking off without knowing exactly how much

If you allow someone else to refuel your airplane, it would be wise to visually verify the fuel level and to reinstall the fuel cap yourself.

fuel you have on board. This is foolhardy and, besides, it is against regulations.

Your preflight should include the removal of the fuel cap(s) for a visual check for the presence of fuel and its level. Verify your eyeball calculation with a dipstick reading (provided you had the foresight to make and calibrate one in the first place).

2. Believing your fuel gauges. You can't rely on fuel gauges. Most of them are inaccurate, at best . . . and like other instruments they can fail to function when you need them the most.

NOTE — I log my tach time when I refuel. Then, before each following flight I check the hours flown since refueling. Knowing that I burn 8 gallons per hour (or whatever), I start looking for a gas station after I have flown 3 hours. My tanks hold 38 gallons. Too conservative, you say? Go ahead and say it . . . but don't try to confuse me with high tech mathematics.

3. The fuel selector valve has caused many an engine-out situation.

For example . . . after the fuel selector is installed, initially, its operation should be viewed with suspicison. What if the handle was installed so it points to the wrong tank? Also, the design of the handle may make you wonder which end is really the pointer. Or worse, what if it is really off and not on any tank position? To play it safe, run the engine long enough on each tank position to allay all doubts. Anytime you have to remove the fuel selector handle, mark it so that it can be reinstalled with the correct alignment. Some handles can go on only one way. Hopefully, that is the way yours is.

4. The pilot forgot to switch tanks and couldn't restart the engine.

5. The fuel tank vent was plugged. Fuel cannot flow if the vent or vent line is plugged with insect larvae accumulations.

You can verify that your fuel tank vent is clear by slipping a short length of plastic tubing over the vent outlet and blowing in it to see if the vent is open.

6. Carburetor ice can do a good job of starving your engine for fuel.

7. Vapor lock is another form of fuel starvation. Due to the formation of vapor and foam bubbles in the fuel lines, insufficient fuel reaches the engine to keep it running even though there is plenty of fuel in the tank.

VAPOR LOCK PREVENTION

Hot weather combined with high engine compartment temperatures can be conducive to the formation of vapor lock in the fuel lines.

You can minimize the risk of vapor lock taking place in your fuel system by:

a. Enclosing the gascolator in a simple aluminum enclosure (shroud) and ducting cooling air through it.

b. Enclosing the engine driven fuel pump in the same manner. The cooling air can be taken from the rear engine baffling.

c. Enclosing engine compartment flexible fuel lines in firesleeves. These will help protect the lines against the high engine compartment temperatures.

d. Protecting fuel lines that pass close to an exhaust stack with simple aluminum heat shields.

The FAA seems to believe that fuel starvation and the forced landing, or crash, that follows are brought on by a lack of proficiency, a lack of familiarity with the fuel system, a lack of attention, a lack of good judgment, or all of the above. In short, except for a few instances of mechanical failure, they are quick to assume that fuel starvation mishaps are due to pilot error.

IT'S TRUE

Finally, if the engine quits, immediately switch to the other tank . . . if you have one. A logical procedure, if you stay calm, cool and collected, isn't it? Maybe that tank has fuel and/or its vent is not plugged.

Would it surprise you, however, to learn that there have been pilots who have experienced engine failure due to fuel starvation, made a forced landing, or a crash landing, only to be informed later by the FAA that they found evidence that the other tank still had fuel at the time of the incident? Did he switch tanks or turn the fuel selector to OFF?

Many builders of the popular Heath Parasol from the 20s and 30s era powered their aircraft with the 27 hp Henderson engine. It was not too reliable. This present day builder installed a more reliable 4-cylinder horizontally opposed engine.

EXHAUST SYSTEMS 9

Exhaust System Notes

When I first started thinking about an exhaust system for my trigear RV-6A, I assumed I would buy a ready-made stainless steel crossover system similar to the one I had installed in my first RV-6 (the taildragger, that is).

That assumption, however, became a quandry after I learned that I could get a complete mild steel exhaust system for about $250 . . . this was considerably less than half the price of the stainless steel exhaust unit I originally had in mind.

Are the stainless steel stacks really that much better? Are they worth the extra cost? Maybe so. But that is not to say that a mild steel exhaust system has a short life or is inferior.

For my part, the cost of either ready-made exhaust system was still more than I had ever expended on any previous project.

Except for one donated ready-made system, all of my earlier projects were fitted with "do it yourself" exhaust stacks of the one type or another.

Somewhere in my distant past, someone convinced me that if an exhaust system lasted 100 hours without failing it would go 1000 hours. I assume that profound utterance applies to the common automotive type mild steel stacks as well.

At any rate, my own experience seems to bear this out because none of my homebuilt engine installations has ever suffered an exhaust system failure. And yet, each exhaust installation was as different from the other as night is from day.

My first airplane, an Emeraude, was fitted with a brand new $28 J-3 exhaust system . . . guess how long ago that was? It never failed.

Another had a liberated Cessna 150 system com-

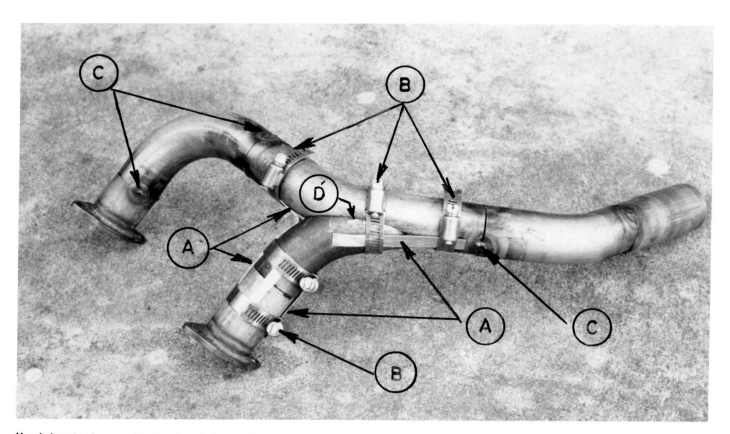

Here's how to clamp and hold exhaust pipe sections in alignment for tack-welding (A). Scrap metal bridging/aligning strips. (B) Stainless steel clamps. (C) Tack-welds (clamps already removed). (D) Exhaust stack joints to be welded.

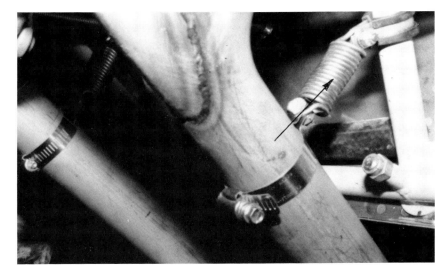

Bracing exhaust pipes against the engine mount or fuselage structure is a poor practice because the engine moves in its shock mounts and the fuselage does not. Result, failed pipes. As shown here the spring may minimize the problem.

plete with two used stainless steel mufflers straddling a set of used stainless stacks. It never failed.

A third was fitted with a scratch built mild steel installation using VW pipes (with lousy welds, yet). Years later, another VW installation did have better welds — but they didn't fail either.

More recently, each follow-on project was economically equipped with homemade stainless steel stacks assembled from used units purchased at fly-ins, or built up of new stainless steel exhaust flanges, straight pipe lengths and preformed elbows. No, I didn't do the welding, a friend Heliarc welded them for me (and, boy, does a builder ever need a skilled friend or two). Again, no failures.

For the life of me I don't know why some of my earlier installations remained trouble-free for the several hundred hours each of them was flown. A little luck, perhaps, and plenty of well located expansion (slip) joints, and properly supported tail pipes, I guess.

Since I have never experienced a failure in either the ready-made or homemade exhaust systems (mild steel or stainless) I have used, I have no preconceived preference for one type of metal over the other.

I do consider myself fortunate that I no longer have to build my own exhaust system and can, if I prefer, purchase a ready-made set from any one of several reliable sources.

A number of these ready-made exhaust systems are designed and custom-fabricated to fit specific aircraft designs — designs like the RV's, T-18's and Mustangs to name a few.

Incidentally, the newsletters, subscribed to by builders for their particular aircraft, are often good information sources for various component parts — including complete exhaust systems.

Naturally, if you prefer, you can still fabricate your own exhaust system using parts available from one of the homebuilder suppliers, or from some local muffler shop.

But, before you can buy a complete system or build your own, you must first decide whether you want to have those expensive stainless steel stacks — or the less expensive mild steel variety.

MILD STEEL VS. STAINLESS STEEL EXHAUST SYSTEMS

Anyway, what difference does it make if you install a mild steel exhaust system instead of a stainless steel system? Your engine won't know the difference. Your pocketbook will though.

I am sure you are aware that the mild steel exhaust pipe installations in automobiles are reliable and hold up very well.

Of course, the prevailing belief among many homebuilders is that mild steel pipes, especially in infrequently flown homebuilt aircraft, are bound to suffer more rust than even those seen in the most abused and neglected cars.

Although the mild steel exhaust pipes will pick up a film of surface rust almost immediately, the assumption that destructive corrosion is quick to follow is not a valid conclusion.

A local VariEze has been flying for years with a mild steel exhaust system that was originally installed eleven years ago. How about that?

I know of stainless steel installations that didn't last half as long . . . they often burned out in and around the mufflers, or suffered cracked exhaust flanges.

Well, now, if rusty pipes offend your senses, you could:

1. Paint the pipes with a high temperature (2,000 degree F. preferably) automotive header paint. Properly done, this high temperature paint is quite effective and will enhance the appearance and prolong the useful life of your automotive pipe exhaust system for many years. Follow the painting instructions carefully. This is the least expensive and most commonly used treatment for protecting mild steel stacks against rust.

2. Have the mild steel pipes coated with Jet-Hot, a relatively new high-temp coating for exhaust systems.

175

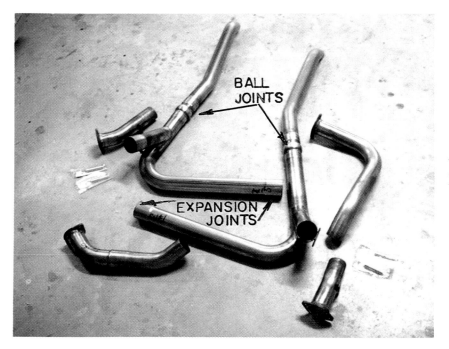

This ready-made exhaust system design has a generous number of expansion joints as well as two integral ball joints for the tail pipes.

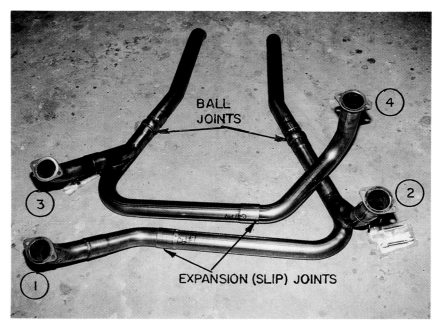

A Bird's eye view of a typical crossover exhaust system. This one uses mild steel automotive pipes. Note that the two front cylinders are interconnected and that the exhaust gases exit through the left tail pipe. The two rear cylinders are also interconnected and exhaust gases exit through the right tail pipe.

3. Have the stacks aluminized.

4. Have the exhaust system chromed.

Sometimes there can be an unexpected advantage to using a mild steel exhaust pipe installation.

For example, in the event you do develop a broken pipe on a cross-country flight, the chances of getting the mild steel pipe welded most anywhere are a lot better than trying to find someone who can repair and reweld stainless exhaust pipes.

A word of caution. Some coated mild steel exhaust pipes may be difficult to repair. Aluminized pipes are probably the worst in this respect. That is, they cannot be reliably re-welded.

It is true. A mild steel exhaust system will be heavier than a similar stainless steel system because the automotive pipes have a heavier (.050") wall thickness. In contrast, stainless steel pipes have a thinner .035" wall thickness. Even so, my ready-made (Vettermann) mild steel crossover exhaust system in the RV-6A weighs only 12 pounds.

The price difference between a mild steel exhaust system and that of a stainless steel system, on the other hand, is considerably greater than the modest weight difference.

That dollar difference alone can make the automotive pipe exhaust system quite irresistible to a budget minded builder — whether he buys or builds his own.

IF YOU HAVE TO BUILD YOUR OWN

If you can buy a ready made exhaust system designed for your aircraft type, I would recommend you get it rather than to try to build your own . . . it might be cheaper in the long run.

There is more to fitting and developing an exhaust system than merely routing the exhaust gases from each cylinder overboard.

John Thorp, designer of the fabulous T-18, used to say that a well designed crossover exhaust system could net a 10% increase in power. However, that may not be true compared to the semi-tuned four pipe exhaust system I bought from Larry Vetterman. It could be true, though, when you compare a crossover system efficiency with that of a common two pipe "Y" branch installation.

When building your own exhaust system, you should realize that if it is improperly done, your exhaust system could suffer from unnecessary power losses due to abnormal back pressures in the system. The installation might even fail after a few hours due to the lack of properly located expansion joints.

What kind of exhaust system would you build? A crossover system? A semi-tuned four pipe exhaust system? Maybe a simple exhaust installation with four short straight stacks? They all work.

However, unless you have the technical background for that sort of thing I would suggest doing it the easy way — duplicate one of the exhaust installations in use in some recent vintage store-bought aircraft.

MAKING YOUR OWN EXHAUST SYSTEM

If you are a careful buyer, or a good scrounger, you can effect significant savings by building your own mild steel exhaust system . . . especially if you can do a creditable job of gas welding the mild steel pipes.

Attempting to weld your own stainless steel exhaust system, on the other hand, may not be as rewarding as it requires special welding techniques, more know-how, and perhaps, some expensive welding equipment.

Although most commercially produced aircraft use expensive mufflers, you will probably fabricate your exhaust system without them to simplify the installation and reduce cost and weight.

The argument made for eliminating mufflers is based on the premise that they are heavy and that homebuilts have very tight fitting cowlings with almost no extra space for mufflers. (Those excuses, incidentally, don't hold water in Switzerland and in other environmentally sensitive countries.)

1. Begin fabricating your exhaust system by making your own mild steel exhaust flanges — or you can simplify the job by purchasing a set to fit your engine (Lycoming or Continental).

2. Start to assemble the component parts by welding the exhaust flanges to short pipe sections about 4"-6" long. Use 1-3/4" dia. pipes for a Lycoming, and a 1-1/2" dia. for most Continentals.

3. Next, temporarily bolt the prewelded exhaust stack stubs to each cylinder. This will establish the correct exhaust flange alignment for each cylinder and will accurately position the stub stacks. The other exhaust system pipes can then be fitted and clamped to these stubs.

4. Decide where to locate the slip joints and ball joints for a trouble-free exhaust system.

5. Cut, fit and clamp each pipe section together.

NOTE — If you think that figuring out how to fit and hold the various pipe sections in place while attempting to assemble and tack weld your exhaust can be difficult, you're right. It is no simple undertaking. The easiest way to do this is illustrated in one of the photos. Notice how the separate pipe sections are clamped together with small metal strips and steel hose clamps to form the assembly. This steel clamp jigging technique is especially effective when you have to work alone.

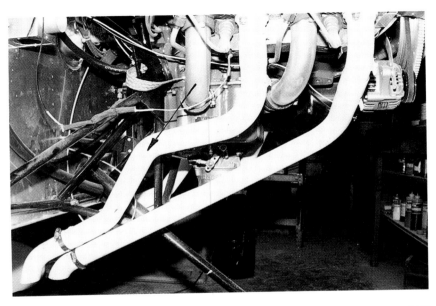

This mild steel four pipe exhaust installation was painted with a high temperature paint as protection against rust. The extra bend in the upper stack would indicate that an attempt was made to tune the pipes, that is, make the lengths equal.

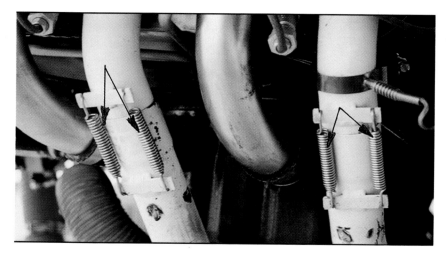

A couple of Yamaha springs are cleverly employed to hold these exhaust slip joints together.

6. After all of the pipe joints have been immobilized with the steel clamps, remove the assembly from the engine and tack weld the joints.

7. After tack welding, reinstall the pipe assemblies on the engine to double check the routing and clearances. Then you can take the tack welded exhaust stacks to your favorite welder and have the welds completed . . . either that or do it yourself.

NOTE — Do not buy or use curved automotive pipe sections that have a rippled or buckled inside radius. You should be able to purchase smoothly bent exhaust pipe sections at most any muffler shop.

You might, on the other hand, find a local shop equipped with mandrels that does custom bending of pipes for hot rodders and the automotive set. This would permit you greater flexibility in obtaining the exact bend radiuses you need in your pipes.

Such a shop can also expand the diameter of one end of a pipe so that it will form a slip joint when assembled with another section of pipe.

AVOIDING EXHAUST SYSTEM FAILURES

Exhaust systems deteriorte and fail because of high engine operating temperatures, vibration that causes metal fatigue in stress concentrated areas, and wear at joints and in clamped connections.

A number of our local area homebuilts have suffered exhaust system problems over the past few years. These problems are quite typical and included cracked exhaust flanges, burned and cracked stacks, and broken tail pipes as well.

Most of the cracks were detected in the welded areas of the exhaust flanges. However, a couple of the aircraft did have exhaust pipes break off completely in flight. Fortunately, no engine compartment fires occurred.

Most of the affected homebuilt owners attributed the failures to the relatively thin walled stainless steel pipe used, and to improper welding technique. Not all the problems were limited to stainless steel exhaust systems.

For my part, however, I believe almost all of the

Short straight stacks are easy to make but they are noisy and may allow engine to cool excessively during letdowns.

failures in homebuilt exhaust systems can be traced to improperly supported tail pipes.

Sometimes, inexplicably, what appears to be an adequately braced installation does develop a crack, or breaks off completely.

In those instances one can only assume that the design and fabrication of the exhaust system didn't provide for properly located expansion joints, and flexible joints that would have allowed the exhaust pipes to expand and contract during normal engine operations.

It is obvious that exhaust system problems are aggravated because they operate under some pretty severe conditions.

For example, the exhaust gases exiting the engine are so hot they heat the pipes red hot . . . about 1400 to 1600 degrees F.

Further downstream, the temperatures are significantly lower causing an uneven heating and expansion along the length of the pipes.

To make matters worse, a sudden cooling of the exhaust pipes caused by prolonged power off letdowns can add still more abuse to the welded joints, and to the entire exhaust system.

I don't recommend wrapping exhaust pipes with one of those automotive "Exhaust Insulating Wrap" kits regardless of the claims made for them. A local Mustang

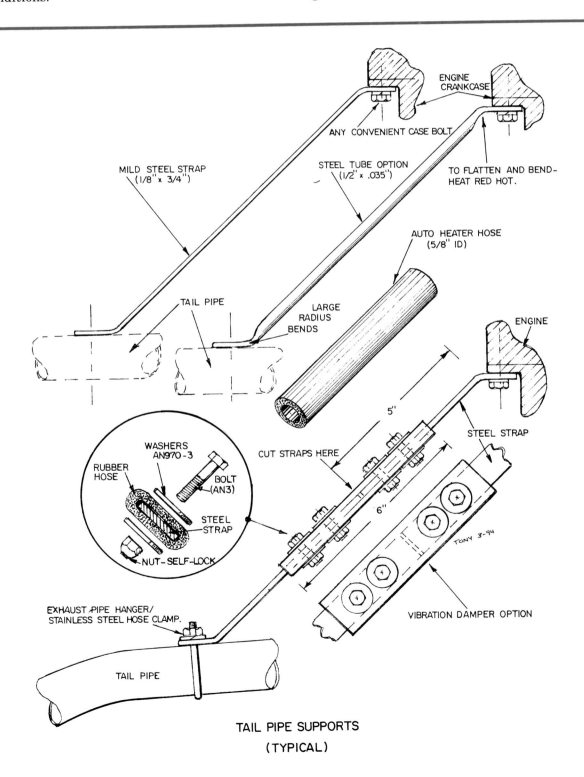

TAIL PIPE SUPPORTS
(TYPICAL)

179

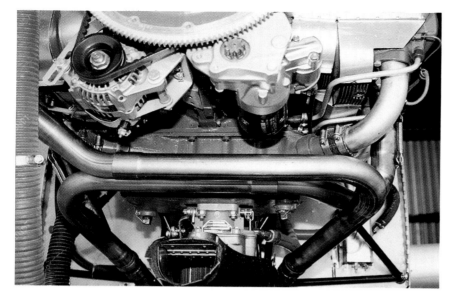

In a crossover exhaust system, both pipes cross in front of the engine crankcase. The close proximity of the hot pipes might influence the engine oil temperature. If that is a problem, the installation of a heat shield between the closest pipe and the crankcase should be considered.

A few more engine compartment details.

Long exhaust pipes are a source of considerable engine compartment heat for a closely cowled engine.

Left — Wrapping the exhaust pipes in aircraft may be a bad idea. Local experience would indicate that burned/failed stacks could result.

Below — How long do you suppose this exhaust system will last without some sort of support for that long heavy tail pipe?

II equipped with a mild steel exhaust system suffered complete failure of the pipes in all of the bend areas. His thermal wrapped pipes had completely burned through.

Do remove your cowling at frequent intervals and carefully inspect the entire exhaust system — inch by inch.

Here are a few things to look for:

1. Exhaust leaks and cracks. These areas usually show up as gray-white streaks.

2. Use new blo-proof or copper asbestos exhaust gaskets when installing or replacing your exhaust system.

Do not reuse the old gaskets! . . .

Install a stainless steel nut with a new star lock washer and a flat steel washer.

Do not over-tighten the exhaust nuts as that might stretch the engine studs.

3. After the first 10 hours of flying time, re-torque the exhaust flange nuts. Be sure you have a plain steel washer and a new star lock washer under each nut.

4. Look for loose or broken clamps and connectors.

5. Check to see that stacks are not dented.

6. Look for cracked or broken stacks and tail pipes.

7. Check heat muffs (and mufflers, if installed) for condition and broken connectors.

8. Be sure the SCAT ducting is in good condition. Use mild steel straps (1/8" x 3/4") or steel tubing (1/2" x .035" wall) from the nearest convenient engine pan bolt to the exhaust pipe support bracket or clamp. A rubber damper of some sort should be considered to dampen and isolate engine vibrations from being transmitted to the exhaust system.

9. Finally, and this is most important, check to see that the exhaust pipes are braced directly to the engine and not to the engine mount or to the fuselage structure.

Remember this . . . the best place to cope with exhaust system problems is on the ground, not in the air!

A FEW EXHAUST SYSTEMS SOURCES

Aircraft Spruce & Specialty Co., PO Box 424, Fullerton, CA 92632, 1-800/824-1930 (for ordering).

Alan Tolle's Custom Aircraft Components, 2920 Staunton Ct., Bakersfield, CA 93306, 805/871-4144.

High Country Exhausts, Larry Vetterman, 7216 S. Pierce Ct., Littleton, CO 80123, 303/932-0561.

Jet Hot Coatings. Three U.S.A. locations offering 72 hr. turnaround time. 1-800/432-3379 (toll free info).

Note the blistered paint on the cowling. This is ample evidence that the exhaust pipes are touching, or are too close to the cowling. The pipes should be fitted with a heat shield. As an alternate measure, cowling may be insulated from the hot pipe(s) by attaching a layer of fire resistant fabric and a metal overlay riveted to the affected areas of the cowl's inner surface. Try to keep exhausts at least 3/4" away from the cowling.

With such shortcomings, what good reasons can you possibly have for using a wood propeller? Plenty . . . but decide for yourself.

Now, the advantages. A fixed pitch wood propeller is the lightest and least expensive type of propeller you can obtain.

Unlike metal propellers, wood blades do not fail from fatigue due to bending. Wood propeller blades are thicker than metal blades and, therefore, do have sufficient stiffness to resist the development of visible flutter which could be destructive.

You can always get a wood propeller designed and custom built to suit your engine and aircraft, whatever it may be. This could be especially important to you folks who have to find a propeller for a pusher. After all, how many type certificated metal pusher propellers are available?

Even a type certificated wood propeller is far less expensive than a similar metal propeller.

In comparing prices, you will find that a fixed pitch metal propeller may cost two to three times more than a custom made wood prop — $2000-$2500, vs $400-$750, approximately. (My beautiful Warnke wood prop — 68 x 69 — cost me $500 plus $30 freight, and a 90 day wait . . . but this was in 1990.).

The waiting period has since been reduced somewhat due to the increased number of custom propeller makers coming on board.

Unfortunately, this has had no appreciable effect on propeller prices. These will, undoubtedly, continue to edge upward through the years.

Wood propellers are noted for their smoother running due to their excellent internal damping characteristics. They also impose less load on the crankshaft.

Wood propellers are constructed of hardwood laminations, the greater the number, the better, because they ensure a stronger propeller and virtually eliminate any tendency for the wood to warp. Laminations as thin as 1/8" also guarantee uniformity of grain and freedom from hidden defects.

CERTIFICATED WOOD PROPELLERS?

Are there such things as type certificated wood propellers? Sure, and one would be my first choice . . . assuming I could obtain such a propeller with the diameter and pitch I needed.

The Sensenich Corporation, in addition to making metal propellers, is perhaps best known by EAAers as a source for the fine type certificated wood propellers used on classic and antique aircraft.

Actually, Sensenich seems to me to be the only U.S. propeller manufacturer who is taking an active role and interest in developing certificated propellers suitable for airplanes like the T-18s, RV-4s, RV-6s, Mustangs and fast composite homebuilts.

With a certificated wood propeller and a type certificated aircraft engine installed, the FAA normally imposes a mere 25 hour mandatory flight test period.

NOTE: I believe that many builders who say they prefer a metal prop over a custom built wood prop are influenced by the knowledge that with the installation of a type certificated aircraft engine, and most any metal propeller, the FAA inspector will grant them a shorter 25 hour test period. Well, as I just pointed out that same privilege also holds true when a type certificated wood propeller is installed in a homebuilt.

You have a decided advantage when you can use a stock certificated wood propeller. Unlike a custom built propeller, you can get one almost immediately from the propeller manufacturer or from your favorite homebuilder supply house.

THE CUSTOM BUILT PROPELLERS

The classified section of SPORT AVIATION lists numerous manufacturers of custom built propellers. Many of them have been in business for years and also have the expertise to advise you in the selection of a suitable propeller.

Even so, for many builders the major deterrent to ordering a custom made (homebuilt) propeller is that the FAA will automatically peg their mandatory flight test period at 40 hours minimum. Understandably, that requirement bugs a lot of builders.

This may not be good news to you. Custom made propellers are seldom stocked and must be made to order.

For this reason, timing can become a very important factor, especially if you delay ordering your custom made propeller until you are ready for it.

Take my advice. Try to anticipate your propeller needs well in advance of the completion date for your airplane. Allow yourself a generous several months lead time. One local RV-6A builder has been waiting for his prop for 5 months.

Almost all of these craftsmen (the custom propeller manufacturers) are turning out wood propellers just as fast as they can . . . and the orders continue to pour in. If present conditions prevail, your wait for a propeller will be long.

WHAT TO EXPECT OF YOUR PROPELLER

Unfortunately, selecting a suitable fixed pitch propeller for any airplane is complicated by the fact that no single fixed pitch propeller (wood or metal) can be best for all flight conditions.

That is to say that a propeller configured to give you the best takeoff and climb will not give you the highest cruise speed and vice versa.

The ultimate performance attainable for a particular aircraft is, in reality, a compromise between the optimum takeoff and optimum cruise performance. Most builders realize this and reluctantly compromise a little bit of cruise for increased efficiency in their rate of climb.

If you will be operating from an unimproved or short airstrip, you, too, will probably consider your rate of climb to be more important than your top speed.

Years ago a Lycoming installation engineer informed me that if I was using a fixed pitch propeller, the static rpm should be 2300, plus or minus 50 rpm, when the engine is rated at 2700 rpm (most Lycomings are).

This static rpm will vary slightly depending on the type of propeller installed. That is, if it is a climb, cruise or economy propeller.

If the static rpm is too high, there is the likelihood of overspeeding the engine at full throttle in level flight.

It is interesting to note that with a constant speed propeller, static rpm will be the rated rpm of the engine. This is controlled by the low pitch setting of the propeller.

The minimum static rpm is established by the manufacturers for each of their engine installations.

Essentially, reaching this recommended minimum static rpm during your engine run up is a fair indication that sufficient power will be developed for takeoff.

A few recommended minimum static rpm for several popular aircraft engines follow:

> Continental A-65 — Not under 1960 rpm
> Continental C-85 — 2200 rpm
> Continental C-90 — 2125 rpm
> Continental O-200 — 2320 rpm
> Lycoming O-235 — 2200 rpm
> Lycoming O-290 — 2200 rpm
> Lycoming O-320 — 2300 rpm

In general, your propeller should be one that gives you the best cruise (full throttle) at approximately 7,500 feet altitude without unduly reducing the rate of climb.

This means a Lycoming with a design 2700 rpm red line should reach its red line rpm with full throttle at that altitude. If the engine overspeeds, your prop could absorb more pitch. If you cannot obtain the 2700 rpm in level flight, the engine is being overloaded by a propeller with too much pitch.

In bragging about their top speed, some builders neglect to mention that they are operating their engines over the red line rpm to get more power. Although this practice may not be regarded as being overly stressful on the engine, I believe engines can endure just so many power strokes between major overhauls.

It's up to you. You can use them up quickly or at a more leisurely rate.

TIPS FOR SELECTING THE RIGHT PROP

A propeller represents a considerable outlay of cash ... even for an uncertificated wood propeller that can only be used on a homebuilt.

That being the case, you had better order the right one the first time. Consider the following:

Your aircraft's weight and balance can influence your propeller selection.

For example, if you find your airplane has a tail heavy condition, a metal propeller would be most beneficial in getting more weight up front. That is because a typical 74 inch metal propeller for a four cylinder Lycoming engine weighs approximately 30 pounds. Compare this to the feather weight 10-12 pounds for an equivalent wood propeller.

Aircraft balance just about mandates the use of a wood prop for most of the popular composite pushers. They cannot tolerate the excessive weight of a metal prop in back.

But that works both ways, doesn't it? If you have a nose heavy condition, substituting a lighter wood propeller in place of a heavier metal prop could help alleviate that problem.

To help you in selecting the right propeller, you'll need to have some basic information about your airplane.

You should, for example, know the maximum diameter propeller you could install and still have a minimum ground clearance (in level attitude) of 9 inches.

You should also know the maximum rpm you could turn a maximum diameter propeller without exceeding its critical tip speed.

The critical tip speed is generally accepted to be 75% of the speed of sound which, at sea level, is 1100 feet per second (at standard temperature and pressure). Above that speed a prop loses efficiency and noise increases considerably.

For this reason, a wood propeller's tip speed should be kept below 850 fps.

With that basic information in hand, you are ready to look for a propeller:

1. You could try to find a type certificated propeller designed for an aircraft that has a design top speed, rated rpm and horsepower similar to what you expect to have.

2. You could rely on the aircraft designer's recommendation for a particular propeller diameter and pitch for each of the engines he has approved. He may even suggest several sources for propellers. You can rest assured that the designer wants his airplane to perform well for obvious reasons. His propeller recommendations should, therefore, be seriously considered.

3. Find out from other builders what props they are using for your type of aircraft. Compare notes with as many of them as you can before ordering. Be prepared to hear conflicting information. The performance figures quoted may not be the same from each of the builders using like propellers. However, you can safely assume that if they are satisfied with the propellers they are flying, a like propeller should be fairly close to what you need.

It's O.K. to be a bit skeptical about performance figures because many builders do not have calibrated instruments and the performance numbers they quote

A certificated propeller is a good choice if you can find one from a type certificated airplane that matches your homebuilt's flight characteristics and if the length is not too great. Ground clearance in level attitude should be at least 9 inches.

Comparing propeller pitches can be confusing. Many prop manufacturers use the flat bottom of the blade in measuring pitch, but some use a zero lift line pitch reference. Hence, one airplane is flying a 58x67 prop while another may be doing no better with a 58x73 prop from another source.

may not be as accurate as they choose to believe.

Tachometers, too, are notoriously inaccurate. Quoted airspeeds especially may be suspect due to poorly located pitot and static ports. Of course, your own instruments should also be suspect unless you have them calibrated and checked for accuracy.

4. Select a propeller maker with a good reputation and rely on his recommendations for a propeller. He will ask you to provide him with some essential information, namely:

What airplane design is the propeller for?

Which engine and horsepower do you have installed?

What's your preference? Best cruise/top speed, best take-off/climb/high altitude or a standard/compromise prop.

What kind of airspeed are you hoping for?

It's comforting to know that most prop makers are very cooperative, and often will repitch your wood prop slightly to fine tune its performance without charge.

And, finally, if your propeller ever develops a serious defect, it should be returned to the manufacturer for repair.

Spinner Safety

It happened, as it frequently does, soon after the application of full throttle for take-off. The loud noise accompanied by a horrendous vibration scared me almost completely out of my wits — leaving just enough awareness to know I had better do something. I immediately throttled back and pulled off the runway into the grass, not knowing if the propeller had thrown a blade or if the engine was self-destructing.

On shut down, I found that it was neither. The back spinner bulkhead had failed at three of its four attachment points, and the spinner was on the verge of parting company with the airplane. Because it didn't break completely loose, the cocked spinner did a thorough job of decimating the front end of the cowling.

Had the spinner broken loose in flight, the consequences could have been more serious, perhaps disastrous, if on parting it had crashed into the windshield or tail surfaces.

This particular spinner failure was attributed to the lack of a front bulkhead (the omission of which was intended to be only 'temporary'), and to an old work-hardened bulkhead with a few tiny undetected old cracks.

The failure occurred approximately 30 hours after the initial installation. And what a surprise it was because the spinner had always tracked perfectly.

This incident lends credence to the belief that propeller spinners are more likely to fail during take-off. Typically, the partially failed spinner will viciously chafe and masticate the cowling until it ultimately separates from the aircraft. It is a frightening experience, one that needs not be repeated to drive home the message. You better believe it — a spinner once installed cannot be ignored . . . not for long anyway.

VIBRATION A WARNING?

The appearance of an unexplained vibration, no matter how infrequent or intense, could be a sign of an impending propeller or propeller/spinner failure. In thinking back, I'm almost certain now that some of the occasional light vibrations I detected were spinner induced and not attributable to improper or excess leaning.

Admittedly, excessive vibration can sometimes be caused by old or deteriorated engine shock mount bushings, improper engine timing, improper leaning, and insufficient engine-to-cowl clearances to name a few culprits. Obviously, excessive and/or prolonged vibration can be harmful to both the propeller and spinner, even if they are not the initial cause of the problem.

Remember, when drilling your spinner kit bulkhead holes, that the holes in the rear bulkhead are larger, usually, ⅝" dia. to accommodate the prop flange driving lugs. Don't drill the large holes through the front bulkhead! Check and see what you need.

The near perfect spinner/cowling profile is easier to achieve if you obtain your spinner first and then build the cowling to match its diameter and curvature. If your cowling is a ready-made one, you are locked in to spinner diameter you can use.

SPINNERS ARE HARD TO INSPECT, BUT . . .

Because spinners are so hard to inspect effectively, any time you have the engine cowling removed you should grab that opportunity to examine your spinner installation . . . from behind. I mean, really **look** at it.

In particular, examine the rear bulkhead for signs of metal distress or incipient cracks.

Another potential source for spinner cracks is in the areas around the propeller cutouts.

Look also at each spinner attachment screw and check for the unwelcome presence of cracks radiating out from under the screw heads.

Maintenance people tell me that many of the older aircraft on which they perform annual inspections can be expected to have had lost screws replaced with a variety of mismatched screws to secure the spinner. Most of the screws will, invariably, be rusty and hard to remove.

During your own annual inspections always replace lost screws with those of the correct length and type. Although the effect of mismatched screws on the balance of a spinner installation might be negligible, it is worthy of note.

Well, so much for you folks with spinners currently in service. Now, if you are a builder who has yet to un-dertake the completion of his first spinner installation, you might find a few tips to be of greater interest to you, so let's compare notes.

Your first thoughts on the subject will, naturally, dwell on the matter of selecting a spinner.

Aircraft Spruce and Specialty Company was one of the first suppliers to make a spinner kit available to the homebuilders. It was sort of an offshoot of Henry Ford's philosophy. That is, you could have any kind you wanted just so long as it was their Bullet Nose Spinner Kit. Thankfully we have come a long way, amigo, and we can now select from a variety of ready-to-use stock spinners manufactured for certificated aircraft, or purchase one of the kit spinners fabricated especially for the homebuilt trade. Indeed, there are all kinds of spinner shapes and sizes from which to select.

READY TO USE STOCK SPINNERS

The ready-to-use spinners, for the most part, are those produced for certificated aircraft (Cessnas, Aeroncas, Luscombes, Pipers, etc.). They are well made and when obtained through homebuilt suppliers are quite affordable. Their greatest appeal is their ease of installation. All you have to do is select a spinner that suits your fancy and fits your engine — then, bolt it on.

A thick metal propeller hub front plate must always be used with a wood propeller.

It is hard to tell if a front bulkhead is installed. Some builders do not use fasteners to secure the front bulkhead to the spinner although common practice dictates otherwise. If no front bulkhead is installed, that lack coupled with the use of countersunk screws could lead to future cracking of the rear bulkhead.

A flimsy backplate, no front bulkhead and a fiberglass spinner would all combine to make this a high risk installation. Fortunately, this gent's friends talked him into installing a front bulkhead.

If ever a propeller installation needed a spinner this one must be it. Not only does a spinner improve the appearance of an airplane, it also, in many instances, improves engine cooling.

This builder may have been more concerned with the rigidity of the rear bulkhead than obtaining the correct fit for the front bulkhead. If the stiffness of the rear bulkhead is not a factor, spacing for the front bulkhead is easier to obtain with a large washer-like spacer cut from aluminum in the required thickness.

The prop cutout is already made and the bulkheads will have been pre-drilled and fitted with nutplates. It should be noted, with relief, that such a spinner will track concentrically and you will not expect to encounter any alignment problems.

There is one thing you should keep in mind though. Since the prop cutout is for a metal propeller, you may have to enlarge the cutout area to accommodate your wood prop. This, however, is a very minor chore compared to preparing a kit spinner blank for installation.

THE KIT SPINNER

Sometimes kit spinners are sold without either a front bulkhead or a rear one. More often only a rear bulkhead is available and you will have to try to locate a front plate (bulkhead) that will fit your propeller hub/spinner combination.

Most, but not all, kit spinners will have the correct size propeller bolt bulkhead holes already drilled or punched out. If the bulkhead blanks are not already pre-drilled, they should, at least, have punch marks to aid in accurately locating the bolt holes that you will

have to drill. Actually, if the holes are not already in place, I would seriously consider buying some other type of spinner.

When ordering your spinner, always specify the type and size engine that it is destined for. The six bolt hole pattern for a small Continental (4.375" between centers) is different from that for a Lycoming (4.750" between centers). So, while both engines, typically, take bulkheads drilled for six 5/8" bushing holes to accommodate the prop shaft drive lugs, remember that a spinner bulkhead will not fit just any engine.

Another thing about buying a spinner. Unless it is large enough to blend into your cowling contours, it will look pathetically small. It will also look ridiculous if the diameter is too large because it would then project beyond the cowling line and into your air inlet area. Know before you order that the quoted spinner diameter is acceptable.

THE BOTTOM LINE

It is important that you realize that many propeller spinner failures occur at relatively low time in service.

Above — The front bulkhead for this spinner was slightly under-sized so the builder layed a strip of tape around its perimeter. He should have, instead, made and installed a plate behind the front bulkhead to move it forward.

Right — On application of power for take-off, three of the spinner attachment points failed causing it to become cocked at an angle. The flailing spinner destroyed the front end of the cowling. Probable cause was attributed to the lack of a front bulkhead and an old fatigued rear bulkhead.

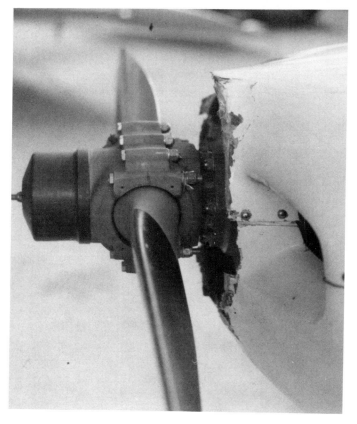

This would indicate that a failed spinner might not have been properly installed and aligned from the very beginning. Also, it is worth noting that large spinners on powerful engines not fitted with a front bulkhead are especially at risk.

In short, I am convinced, now, that anyone who installs a spinner without a proper fitting front bulkhead is begging for fate to take a swat at him.

For other information, see "Installing Spinners," January 1976 Sport Aviation.

Cut the prop blade openings undersized using a saber saw. Then, slip the spinner over the prop to see where it needs to be trimmed. Note the alignment mark (A).

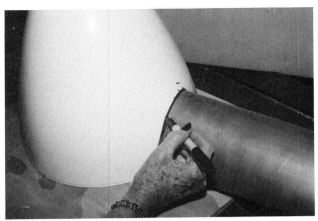

Trace around the spinner cutout with a marker pen to determine where it needs to be trimmed and how much.

After a good spinner fit is obtained, jam it on tight and clamp it to the back bulkhead with small C-clamps or Cleco shoulder clamps for an alignment check.

This shows how the spinner alignment pointer is used to align the spinner before the attachment screw holes are drilled. The same pointer can be lowered and used to check that the propeller blades track within 1/16" of each other.

Shown here is how the 832 anchor nuts are held in place with Cleco clamps while you drill the rivet attachment holes. Note the alignment mark on the back bulkhead flange.

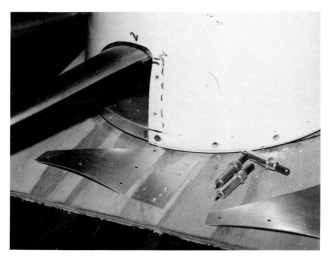

These are the pieces needed to close that large gap behind the propeller.

The front bulkhead flange must be cut away in two places to clear the propeller blades.

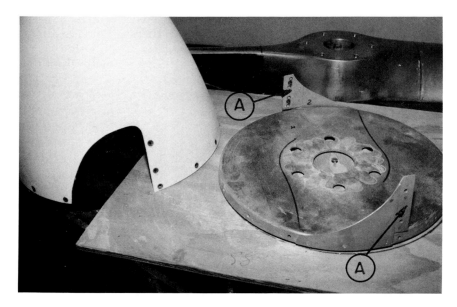

Shown here is how the gap seals are riveted to the back bulkhead. The nut plates (A) permit the spinner to be removed.

2. Next, make an accurate template to use for cutting out the propeller hub opening in the spinner. Most any stiff material (manila folder, aluminum flashing, etc.) you can cut with scissors can be used to make your template for the prop hub cut-out.

3. Cut out a rough "eyeball" approximation of the opening in the template material you are using.

4. Refine it by bridging the gaps with pieces of masking tape. Mark your template, "This Side Up".

5. Establish a reference line anywhere on the spinner by drawing a short line up from its base using a square for alignment.

6. Then position your template against the vertical line drawn on the spinner and trace the blade cut-out outline onto the spinner. This will establish the spinner cut-out for one of the propeller blades.

7. Measure around the base of the spinner to a point

180 degrees opposite and trace the same outline on the opposite side of the spinner. Be sure to keep the same template face side up for both tracings. Now, you are ready to cut out the two blade openings in the spinner.

MAKING THE BLADE CUTOUTS

Clamp a short 2 x 4 to the end of your workbench to use as a support for the spinner while you are cutting the openings.

You may find it less risky to make your cut-outs with a hand-held hacksaw blade or a nibbler. I prefer to use a saber saw, fitted with a fine tooth metal cutting blade.

It is extremely important that you cut **well inside the lines** just to be safe. You will be trying for a uniform 1/16" to 1/8" clearance between the cut-outs and the prop hub. Don't try for a tight fit as the spinner might, later, cut into the propeller. Proceed slowly and check the fit against the propeller frequently.

After the two initial openings are rough cut out, the repetitious "trial fit and trim" work begins.

Essentially, you start by lowering the spinner over the jigged propeller/bulkhead assembly to see how it fits. Since your preliminary propeller hub blade cut-outs are well undersized, it will not slide down very far before some part of the cut-out hits on the propeller hub.

With a "Sharpie" marking pen, trace along the prop hub marking where the spinner hits it (touches).

Remove the spinner and slip it over the protruding end of that 2 x 4 support clamped to your workbench. This will support the spinner while you grind away the ink marks with a rotary file.

Replace the spinner on the prop. Mark it again. Trim it again.

Repeat the process until you have a perfect fit with approximately a 1/16" gap between the spinner and the prop hub. Be sure to file and sand away all tool marks.

The spinner must not contact the propeller anywhere!

Although some large stock spinners have the prop cut-outs flanges, I would not recommend that you try to duplicate the same on your spinner. You will only induce stresses by stretching the metal and probably leave ugly tool marks that could become starting points for cracks.

Likewise, I would not recommend riveting in doubler reinforcements around the cut-out edges — or epoxying them in as one builder suggested. Along that line, if you have seen doublers in spinners I am sure it was because someone was trying to salvage a cracked spinner . . . another impulsive idea that should never take wing.

DOES THE FRONT BULKHEAD FIT?

Now that the spinner shell fits around the propeller perfectly, remove it and add the front bulkhead to your propeller jig assembly.

You will, however, have to cut away part of the flange on each side of the front bulkhead before it will lay flush against the propeller hub. Reassemble your jig assembly by placing the front bulkhead on top of the propeller and reinstalling the 6 propeller bolts to maintain alignment.

Once again, slide the spinner over the prop/bulkhead assembly and see how the front bulkhead fits.

But, how can you tell? You can't see inside the spinner.

Well, for one thing, if the spinner shell will not slide down all the way to the bottom edge of the back bulkhead's flange, you will know the front bulkhead diameter is too big.

But, what if the spinner dome does slide down and fits perfectly flush with the back bulkhead? Does that mean the front bulkhead is contacting the spinner properly?

Not really . . . it could be a sign it is too small and not even touching the spinner. Here's how you can tell.

Remove the front bulkhead and place a spacer washer over each propeller bolt hole.

Replace the front bulkhead over the washer spacers and reinstall the spinner dome.

If the bottom rim of the spinner still fits flush with the back bulkhead, you know that the front bulkhead is still NOT contacting the spinner shell as it should.

Remove the spinner and front bulkhead again, and add another spacer washer all around. Repeat the process until you detect that the spinner shell will no longer fit flush with the back bulkhead's flange.

Measure the total thickness of the spacer washers used and you will know how much the front bulkhead must be moved forward to have a tight fit of the front bulkhead inside the spinner.

Instead of using that short stack of washers, you can make a substitute set of 6 aluminum spacers . . . that way you won't forget how many washers it takes.

Alternatively, you can make a special large diameter aluminum spacer plate if the correction required is not much more than 3/16" or so thick. Otherwise, it might be better to obtain a larger diameter front bulkhead . . . if you can find one.

If this problem involves a fiberglass spinner, you might be able to lay up several additional layers of fiberglass around the inside of the spinner to compensate for the too small diameter of the front bulkhead.

FRONT BULKHEAD MODIFICATION

Some RV-6 builders learned that when they replaced a wood propeller with a metal Sensenich prop, their spinner had to be replaced because the propeller blade openings were too big.

They also discovered when fitting the new spinner, the front bulkhead diameter was much too small to be used as is. No replacement bulkhead was available, or in the offing at that time. What to do?

The undersized front bulkhead would have to be moved forward almost an inch (as already described) before it would contact the spinner shell.

Some bright soul figured that if he turned the front bulkhead over, it would almost fit . . . but not quite. Now, it was slightly too big. Since the front bulkhead flange would now be facing forward he didn't consider that to be a problem but, rather, a solution to the fitting problem.

The front bulkhead flange could be shrunk enough to fit perfectly. This shrinking was done in the best metal working tradition using a hammer and a back-up bucking bar.

Because the front bulkhead becomes hardened during its manufacture, it is a good idea to anneal it before you start banging on it to shrink its diameter.

The annealing process is very simple.

Use a lighted candle (or acetylene torch) to coat the bulkhead flange area with black soot. Then, with a

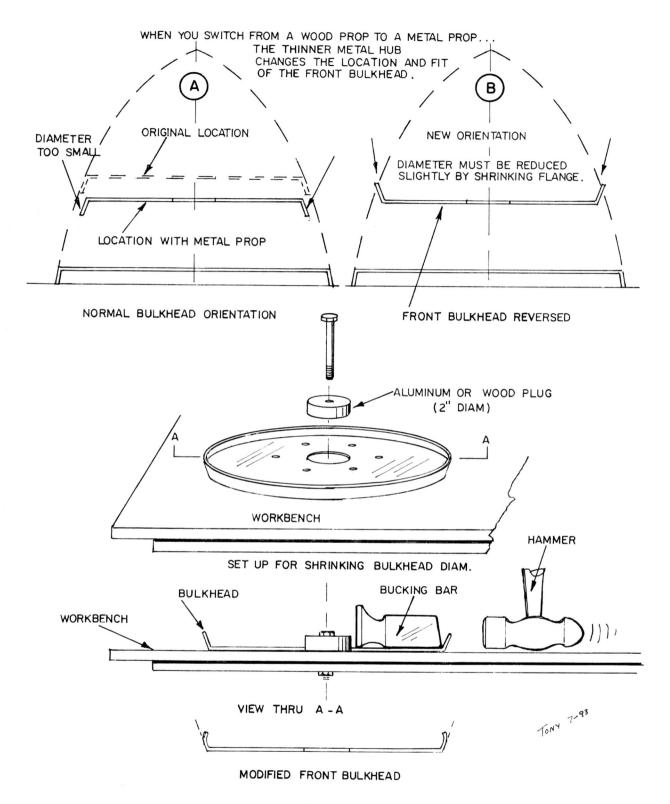

WHEN YOU SWITCH FROM A WOOD PROP TO A METAL PROP...
THE THINNER METAL HUB
CHANGES THE LOCATION AND FIT
OF THE FRONT BULKHEAD.

A

B

DIAMETER TOO SMALL

ORIGINAL LOCATION

NEW ORIENTATION

DIAMETER MUST BE REDUCED SLIGHTLY BY SHRINKING FLANGE.

LOCATION WITH METAL PROP

NORMAL BULKHEAD ORIENTATION

FRONT BULKHEAD REVERSED

ALUMINUM OR WOOD PLUG (2" DIAM)

A

A

WORKBENCH

SET UP FOR SHRINKING BULKHEAD DIAM.

HAMMER

BULKHEAD

BUCKING BAR

WORKBENCH

VIEW THRU A - A

TONY 7-93

MODIFIED FRONT BULKHEAD

FIGURE 2.
FRONT BULKHEAD MODIFICATION

Don't use Teflon tape on any fuel line pipe threads as particles of the tape sometimes finds their way into the fuel system and show up on the screens.

Chafing, if caught in time, is of no consequence and is actually a testimonial to good inspection and maintenance.

FUEL EXHAUSTION

Fuel exhaustion means you just ran out of fuel. Your engine has stopped and your immediate prospects are, (1) a successful forced landing, or (2) a crash landing.

Precautions you can take to avoid such a situation:
Know your fuel system.
Know how much fuel you have on board.
Know your fuel consumption.

Be sure your refueling destination will have fuel and will be open for business (check your Airport/Facility Directory — issued every 8 weeks).

Don't trust fuel gauges.

Some pilots run a fuel tank dry as a routine practice. This technique should be avoided as the engine will stop. A fuel injected engine requires a longer restart effort than does a carbureted one. Meanwhile, loss of precious altitude and an undesirable sudden cooling may result in potential engine damage . . . or even a forced landing.

Fuel exhaustion, whatever the cause, invariably has serious consequences.

"Are you having fun yet?"

Carl Schuppel

This Cozy cruises at 210 mph at 65% power burning seven
and a half gallons of gas per hour. It is powered with a
180 hp Lycoming O-360A1A engine, with a 3-blade, 78" pitch,
64" dia. prop installed. Builder devised and built an intake
plenum that fits in stock Cozy cowl to fit this engine installation. A 4-pipe exhaust system was also devised.

The EAA Flight Advisor Program, introduced during the 1994 EAA Fly-In Convention at Oshkosh, is aimed at providing service to EAA members and helping to improve sport aviation safety.

With the growth of sport aviation activity, it became increasingly important to have an organized support group for those making their early flights in home-built and restored aircraft. The Flight Advisor Program uses the vast flying experience of EAA members to help a fellow member organize and conduct a safe flight test plan.

Accidents in the early phases of flying a new airplane usually occur because of the inexperience or lack of currency in type. It's important for pilots to know what they are looking for in the initial flights and have a comprehensive plan to operate the aircraft. Inexperienced pilots may experience instances where an airplane will handle differently than expected, or not know where to turn for help and hope everything turns out OK.

EAA Flight Advisors are designed to be that resource. The individual Flight Advisor works strictly with flight-oriented questions in all types of aircraft, from antiques to ultralights. They advise and assist in making evaluations, allowing the pilot to make the final go/no-go decision. The builder/pilot always holds the final decision and will be responsible for flying the aircraft.

The Flight Advisor's role includes:
- helping the pilot evaluate his or her current proficiency and skill;
- assist in analyzing the airplane to be flown against the pilot's skill level;
- comparing the pilot's skill to that required by the airplane;
- aid in finding proper instruction, if necessary;
- assist in the planning of the first several flights of the airplane, using preplanned schedules.

Each Flight Advisor is selected and designated because of experience in a number of specific flight areas. Each Advisor has special areas of expertise, depending on his or her background. They include pilots and builders of all ages. That means pilot/builders can take advantage of the considerable flight experience with EAA's membership, even among the sizable percentage that no longer hold current medical certificates.

With the Flight Advisor's assistance and evaluation, it is hoped the builder/pilot will come to an informed decision whether to fly the new airplane or seek more instruction. If more flight instruction is needed, the Flight Advisor will provide criteria for evaluating the proper instructor and training aircraft.

EAA Flight Advisors are experienced in a wide variety of aircraft types and configurations. Their experience is supported by a growing amount of material to help the pilot/builder evaluate the skills needed to fly safely and enjoyably.

The challenge of a first flight is often a daunting one. EAA Flight Advisors are ready to share their extensive flight background with others, becoming a resource that can help aviation and aviation safety grow in the years ahead. In addition to EAA's primary insurance carrier providing a discount in your premiums if you have at least three (3) visits from EAA Technical Counselors during the course of construction, by utilizing the EAA Flight Advisor Program when your project is ready for flight, EAA's primary insurance carrier will even cover the first ten (10) takeoffs and landings.

For more information on the EAA Flight Advisors program, write to EAA Flight Advisors, P.O. Box 3086, Oshkosh, WI 54903-3086, or call (414) 426-4800.

EAA
VIDEOS
&
PUBLICATIONS

Aircraft Welding (45 min.)   *21-36687*
Great introduction for the novice or a refresher for experienced welders. Learn how to run a bead, read a puddle, tack weld, cluster weld and much more!

Building Your Own Airplane: CORROSION (60 min.)   *21-38113*
Corrosion threatens every aircraft exposed to humid conditions and acid rain. Learn from Geo Hindall how to recognize, prevent and protect your aircraft against corrosion.

Aircraft Painting (60 min.)   *21-36467*
Join a professional paint crew as they show you the detailed steps and techniques involved when painting an aircraft.

Building Your Own Airplane (40 min.)   *21-10429*
Answers many of the questions on what project to select, tools and skills required, construction time, documentation, inspection, insurance and other factors to consider when building. Ideal for first time builders.

Fabric Covering With Ray Stits (120 min.)
    21-36141
Learn the delicate art of fabric covering from the expert — Ray Stits (EAA #136) — the man who developed the popular Stits Poly-Fiber Aircraft Coating process. Step by step instructions.

"How-To" Videos to Help You Build

There's nothing like a visual demonstration when learning new skills. These videos take the mystery out of aircraft building by demonstrating the most efficient techniques of building an aircraft, welding, covering, painting or maintaining aircraft.

Aircraft Welding (120 pgs)   *21-37864*
Fundamental welding techniques for the building & repair of aircraft, from the pages of Sport Aviation and other sources. 120 pages filled with aircraft welding tips and information.

Wood Aircraft Building Techniques (140 pgs) *21-18100*
Excellent resource book on "How To" build or repair wood aircraft.

Custom Built Sport Aircraft Handbook (144 pgs) *21-13510*
A guide to construction standards for the amateur aircraft builder and detailed information on FAA contact and applicable FARs.

Flying and Glider Manuals
Reprints of original "Building and Flying Manuals" published from 1929 to 1933 by Modern Mechanix and Inventions.

1929 Flying & Glider Manual   *21-14167*
Contains information on flight lessons plus building the Heath Super Parasol, Russell-Henderson Light Monoplane and an easy to build glider.

1930 Flying & Glider Manual   *21-14168*
Plans for building a Heath Baby Bullet, set of light plane metal floats; building the Northop Glider, Lincoln Biplane, Alco Sportplane, plus other tips on building and welding.

1931 Flying & Glider Manual   *21-14169*
Building the "Longster", Georgias Special, a glider and secondary glider, Driggs Dart, the Church Midwing, the Heath Seaplane Parasol and its pontoons, the Northop Glider and other gliders.

1932 Flying & Glider Manual   *21-14170*
Building the Pietenpol Aircamper with Ford motor conversion,

Powell "P-H" Racer, the Heath Super Soar Glider, Penquin practice plane, Ramsey "flying bathtub" and other designs. Also, constructing a hangar.

1993 Flying & Glider Manual   *21-14171*
Building the Gere Sport Biplane, Pietenpol floats, Pietenpol Sky Scout, and Henderson Longster. Also, Long Harlequin Motor plans, a hydroglider and info on building propellers.

Amateur-Built Aircraft Service And Maintenance Manual   *21-17140*
Prepared by the Experimental Aircraft Association for the Technical Counselor/builder, owner, operator and those who service amateur-built aircraft. Provides a guide with important facts about your airplane. Information and descriptions of structural, mechanical and material details with reference to proper servicing and operation.

EAA Aircraft Log Books   *11-13137*
Especially prepared by EAA. Provides space for entries that are not found in "Standard" log books, and deletes many of the features of military and commercial logs not applicable to recreational aircraft.

EAA Pilot Log Book   *11-16552*
Meets the special needs of the sport and recreational flyer.

EAA Engine And Reduction Drive Log Book   *11-13951*
Can be used for certificated or non-certificated engine records. Includes a special section for reduction unit data.

In addition to the videos and publications listed here, EAA offers many, many others that cover design, flying, historical, military, aerobatic, air racing and a great selection of special interest aviation subjects. Write or call for your free catalog.

Order from: EAA CATALOG SALES, P.O. Box 3065, Oshkosh, WI 54903-3065

CALL TOLL FREE 1-800-843-3612 (OR 414-426-4800 • FAX 414-426-4873)
MAJOR CREDIT CARDS ACCEPTED

Notes:

Easy to Reach:

The EAA Aviation Center is located off Hwy. 41 at the Hwy. 44 exit Oshkosh, WI — adjacent to Wittman Regional Airport.

Museum Hours:

Open Monday thru Saturday 8:30 a.m. to 5:00 p.m.

Sunday 11:00 a.m. to 5:00 p.m.

Visit the EAA Air Adventure Museum

Visit the world's largest, most modern sport aviation museum. Over 90 full size aircraft on display many rare, historically significant aircraft. Prototypes of some of sport aviation's most successful designs. See World War I fighters, antiques, classics, and business aircraft of the 30s — racers, experimental and aerobatic aircraft, ultralights and more! See exact replicas of the 1903 Wright "Flyer" and Lindbergh's "Spirit of St. Louis". View the impressive art and photo galleries, historical artifacts, audio-visual presentations and four unique theatres. Enjoy the barnstormer era that comes to life seasonally at the Pioneer Airport adjacent to the museum — and visit the new Eagle Hangar that honors the aviators of World War II and displays many of the famous aircraft flown in combat. Great gift shop too!

EAA *AIR*
ADVENTURE
MUSEUM™
OSHKOSH, WI

EAA AVIATION FOUNDATION

EAA Aviation Center ● Oshkosh, WI 54903-3086 ● 414-426-4800

Notes:

START HERE!

Each month valuable information on a variety of technical subjects about designing, building or flying homebuilts, light aircraft or ultralights. EXPERIMENTER keeps you up to date on what's happening in sport aviation — what others are building — what new designs are being developed — building techniques for composite, wood, metal, tube or fabric structures — performance data — flight safety — and a wealth of regular features you'll find invaluable. Learn the right way from the experts.
Be sure to get EXPERIMENTER every month!

The "How To" Magazine for the Aircraft Builder

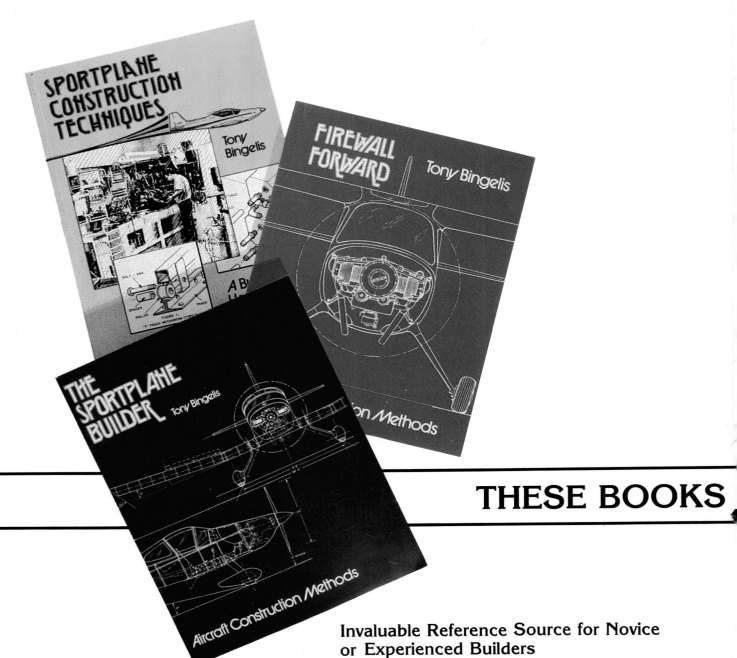

THESE BOOKS

Invaluable Reference Source for Novice or Experienced Builders

Don't build without these three publications — a wealth of practical information for anyone designing or building an aircraft.

Firewall Foreward (308 pgs)   *21-13950*
By Tony Bingelis. Manual on piston engine installations. One of the best engine reference manuals for the amateur builder.

Sportplane Builder (324 pgs)   *21-30140*
By Tony Bingelis (Vol. I) Aircraft construction methods and techniques for the homebuilder. Articles taken from Tony's columns in Sport Aviation magazine.

Sportplane Construction Techniques (372 pgs)
                                                    21-01395
By Tony Bingelis. (Vol. II) More aircraft construction tips for the homebuilder. Articles taken from Tony's columns in Sport Aviation magazine.